D1048591

Managing Stress

Jane Cranwell-Ward has had eighteen years experience of lecturing on stress and personnel-related subjects. Until recently she was based at Kingston Business School but is now deputy director of In-Company Programmes at Henley, The Management College.

Jane Cranwell-Ward has also done much consultancy work for various national and international companies as well as for some local authorities.

Jane Cranwell-Ward

Managing Stress

Pan Original
Pan Books London Sydney and Auckland

First published 1987 by Pan Books Ltd,
Cavaye Place, London SW10 9PG
9 8 7 6 5 4 3 2 1
© Jane Cranwell-Ward 1987
ISBN 0 330 29668 X

Printed and bound in Great Britain by Richard Clay Ltd, Bungay, Suffolk

For
my mother,
Pippa and Neil
for their help
and support

Acknowledgements

I should like to thank all those who have helped to develop my ideas and thoughts for this book. In particular, thank you to all the managers who completed questionnaires and were interviewed. The case material collected proved invaluable. Thanks are also due to the organizations that gave me the opportunity to run stress management workshops.

I should also like to thank all the students and my former colleagues at Kingston Polytechnic. Their contribution during the development of the exercises for the book was greatly appreciated.

During the final stages of writing the book my discussions with colleagues at Henley, The Management College, helped its completion. I am particularly grateful to Roger Oldcorn for suggesting I should write the book in the first place, and for his support throughout.

A special thank you goes to Dave Francis. I am grateful for his creative ideas, precision with words and his help and support, particularly during the stressful periods!

Finally, I would like to thank Liz Wolfenden and Linda Robinson for their help with the typing, and Stephanie Gale-Burkitt for her valuable assistance.

Contents

Introduction

Managing Stress has been written to help you, the manager, develop the skills of effective stress management. I am very aware that many people suffer from stress, including those at more junior levels, and you may discover that your subordinates are suffering from stress. This book will also help you to develop strategies for coping with their stress, and they too will benefit from reading it. While I have written *Managing Stress* for the manager, much of the material has proved useful and relevant to people in non-managerial positions. The symptoms of stress are likely to be identical whether you are employed as a manager, teacher or dentist. Strategies for managing stress will also be equally applicable.

This book should give you information which enables you to cope with stress more effectively and to avoid the negative consequences of excessive stress. If you are suffering from stress, want to learn why, and how to manage it, then this is the book for you.

Managing Stress has been written in the form of a workbook. The format is explained fully in the section entitled How to use the book (page 4). It is written in a practical, down-to-earth way, and requires your commitment and active involvement in completing the exercises. You will then develop a deeper understanding of stress, and an awareness of yourself, your vulnerability and reactions to stress through diagnosis and reflection. You will be helped to manage stress by establishing and maintaining balance in your life, and developing appropriate coping strategies.

I should like to define 'manager'. He or she is a person who has control over resources, including other people. I use the term in its broadest sense to include, for example, engineers acting as team leaders, ward sisters managing other nurses, and senior accountants coordinating the work of more junior staff.

'Stress' is difficult to define and you need to be perfectly clear as to how I use the term. For this reason Step Three of the book will deal exclusively with understanding stress, including its physiological background, and will provide the conceptual framework for the rest of the book. I have taken the view that stress results when a person's perceived or actual capabilities and resources are insufficient to meet the demands of the situation. In other words, stress is the result of imbalance.

'Managing' also needs to be defined. *Collins English Dictionary* defines it as 'exercising control'. 'Managing stress' could therefore be seen as the controlling of a situation in which an imbalance is perceived between demands, and capabilities and resources.

Most people regard stress as something negative, but in learning to manage stress effectively you may come to believe that the experiences of stressful periods in your life can actually be beneficial. Stress, if channelled in the right way, can provide the energy for increased performance and self-development.

Few managers can afford to ignore the effects of stress. More days are lost from work through stress-related illness than are lost as a result of strike action. Medical experts have clearly demonstrated that stress is a killer: there is a high correlation between excessive stress and coronary heart disease. Numerous other illnesses are stress-related, as you will find out in Step Six.

Many books have already been written on the subject of stress. Some are written from an organizational perspective and deal at length with the symptoms and causes of stress, while the management of stress is treated in a rather detached way. Other books are written by medical experts and concentrate on stress-related illness and ways of achieving a healthy life. Few seem to adopt the self-help approach needed to develop the skills of stress management.

My interest in the subject has developed from training and lecturing to large numbers of practising managers, including personnel managers. I also have a personal interest in the subject, having suffered from excessive stress in the past, and while writing this book! I now feel more able to manage stress successfully and hope others will benefit from some of the experience I have gained over the years.

I was motivated to write a book on stress partly by managers attending qualification courses at Kingston Polytechnic. Several of them commented that there was no readable book on stress management. I felt encouraged to fill the gap.

The material included in this book is based largely on question-naires completed by 200 managers and on in-depth, follow-up interviews conducted with a smaller group. These experiences of stress are included at several points in the book in the form of case histories. Names have been changed to protect those who gave their time so willingly.

A few years ago stress management was regarded as something required only by the inadequate few. Today, professional athletes, tennis players and musicians have all learnt the value of managing stress levels to achieve peak performance. By following the steps outlined in *Managing Stress* you could help yourself to become a more effective manager.

How to use the book

There is no one right way to manage stress. Instead there are a wide range of possible options, some of which will be suitable for you. This is the principle upon which this book is based.

Managing Stress is written in the form of a workbook. This means that you are required to take an active part, firstly in completing exercises to diagnose factors relevant to understanding stress, then in working out your own self-development programme to manage stress effectively.

You need not read the book from cover to cover immediately – unless, of course, you feel your problem is very urgent! A better alternative is to work through the book more slowly, allowing time for reflection and discussion with colleagues, your spouse, or friends. This will help you to develop a broader perspective on yourself and the way you currently manage stress.

You may decide to work through the book with others. After seminars on stress management, people often tell me they have discussed the exercises with colleagues and friends. The strategies that evolve from shared reflection seem to be far more successful than those arrived at when the task is tackled in isolation.

I believe that acquiring the skill of managing stress requires commitment and involvement on the part of the reader. Self-understanding and carefully chosen strategies, on the basis of diagnosis, result in successful stress management. Although you don't necessarily need to read the book from cover to cover, do try to resist the temptation to skim past the exercises, intending to complete them tomorrow.

To be able to make full use of *Managing Stress* you need a clear idea of its structure.

The book is divided into four separate sections:

- In Part One you will work through a series of exercises designed to help you understand factors that are relevant to stress management.
- In Part Two you will review and consolidate what you have learnt from the previous section and consider the implications for managing stress.
- In Part Three you will consider various strategies and techniques used to cope with stress.
- In Part Four you will plan your strategy.

Within these four sections there are eleven steps, briefly described below, which you complete:

Part One – Diagnosis and understanding

Step One: Disposition and stress

The stance you take in a situation is partly dependent on your disposition. You may thrive on a lot of excitement in your life, or you may prefer fairly calm conditions. You need good self-insight to identify your own balance. This first step will give you the necessary insight.

Step Two: Assessing vulnerability to stress

Developing resistance to stress is important. Managers are becoming much more health conscious, which should help them become more resistant to the impact of stressful situations. Many managers drink less at lunchtime, count calories and take more exercise. Some have become actively involved in a sport, or have taken up jogging. In Step Two you will be given the opportunity to assess your vulnerability to stress. Managing stress successfully often requires you to make adjustments to your total lifestyle.

Senior management are also developing a growing awareness of the importance of stress and its impact on employees. More employees are being referred to centres for health and fitness tests. Stress management courses are being run, and stress counselling provided for staff. Large organizations are also beginning to provide facilities such as gymnasiums and swimming pools to help employees get fit and maintain fitness levels.

Step Three: Understanding stress

Stress was defined in the Introduction as an imbalance between capabilities and demands. When this imbalance occurs physiological and psychological changes take place. To increase your understanding of stress these changes will be fully described in Step Three.

Step Four: Diagnosing the causes of stress

As managers you are probably faced with a range of stressful situations, but stress is not only with you at work – it permeates every aspect of your life. For example, one in three marriages ends in divorce. Divorce is ranked very high as a cause of excessive stress. Once excessive stress is experienced the body reacts defensively and the negative effects of stress remain with you at work and at home. Step Four will focus on sources of stress applicable to both situations.

Step Five: Assessing the level of change in your life

Organizations are undergoing rapid technological change: this results in feelings of uncertainty and insecurity. To cope with change you may need to be retrained, redeployed or even made redundant. You could be facing any one of these changes at the moment. Step Five will give you the opportunity to calculate the amount of change – good and bad – that has been going on in your life recently, and will provide a measure of the demands placed upon you.

Step Six: Spotting the warning signs

Effective managers need to be aware of increasing pressure and able to recognize the symptoms. How can you spot the signs of excessive stress? Do you sometimes feel unwell and unable to cope, or unable to think straight? You are not alone. Many managers have reported similar feelings. You may be aware of the warning signs. Others who suffer may be less able to recognize the signs, or are less prepared to admit that they are suffering from the effects of excessive stress.

The impact of stress is not restricted to illness. It also has a detrimental effect on important functions of management, such as the effectiveness of decision making, the quality of interpersonal relationships, the standard of work, the quality of working life and, ultimately, the level of productivity. You will be encouraged to recognize your own indicators of excessive stress so that you can take the appropriate action quickly, thus preventing a build-up of harmful effects.

Part Two – Review and consolidation

Step Seven: Weighing up the balance and developing a vision of the future

This step follows on logically from Section One. Having completed your diagnosis you need to spend some time reflecting back on the data. In particular, you need to assess the demands in your life at the moment and your capabilities and resources for meeting the pressure. This, along with the review of the signs of stress, will help you assess your stress level.

You then need to set aside some time to think about the future. What are the implications for managing stress?

When you have completed this step you should be clear about your future needs. This will help you select the most appropriate strategy for managing stress.

Part Three – Strategies and techniques for managing stress

Step Eight: Optimizing stress levels

Reference has already been made in the Introduction to the positive effects of stress. One important way of managing stress is to flow with the pressure and maximize performance. Two factors influence the way you react to stress: your level of competence, and the level of challenge in the situation. Your reaction is also influenced by self-confidence and your level of commitment to and control over the situation. This step will help you identify your reactions to situations and will also help you develop a way of working to maximize performance.

Step Nine: Recognizing ineffective coping strategies

Some managers suffer from excessive stress because they use ineffective coping strategies. There are several strategies which actually correlate with stress-related illnesses and which are far from effective at reducing the effects of stress. You need to be aware of these methods in case you use any of them. They are best avoided in future.

Step Ten: Strategies to remedy imbalance

As I mentioned earlier there are a range of strategies available for managing stress. Your choice will be influenced by the diagnostic work completed in the first section. Step Ten will list the available strategies and will give advice on the strategy most suited to your personal circumstances. Once you have chosen the strategy you will then be able to study it in more detail before moving to the final step.

Section Four – Managing the balance

Step Eleven: Your stress management strategy

In the final step you will identify what needs to be done to implement the strategy you have selected. This is obviously an important step, and will ensure that you take action and evaluate the outcome.

The steps follow a logical sequence. To complete the process you will need to undertake each one in order, from One to Eleven. The relationship between the steps is shown in Figure 1.

One final word of explanation. The questions and exercises in this book have been designed as self-help activities, not scientifically validated questionnaires. For this reason, use them to help you reflect, and then come up with your own assessments, rather than regarding the results as absolute measurements.

Further reading is suggested at the end of the book. Managing stress should not be viewed as an activity isolated from the rest of your life. You may need to develop additional skills – such as time management and interpersonal skills – and one book cannot cover all these areas in sufficient depth. *Managing Stress*

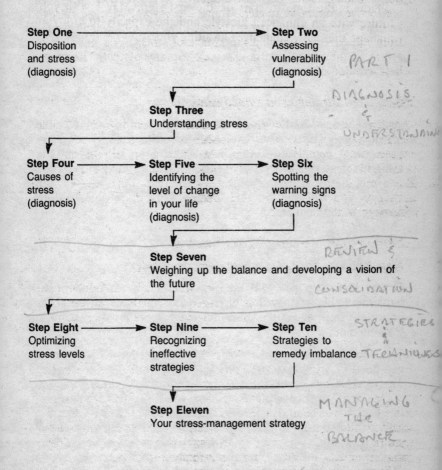

Figure 1 **Managing Stress**

Step One
Disposition
and stress
(diagnosis)

Step Two
Assessing
vulnerability
(diagnosis)

Step Three
Understanding stress

Step Four
Causes of
stress
(diagnosis)

Step Five
Identifying the
level of change
in your life
(diagnosis)

Step Six
Spotting the
warning signs
(diagnosis)

Step Seven
Weighing up the balance and developing a vision of
the future

Step Eight
Optimizing
stress levels

Step Nine
Recognizing
ineffective
strategies

Step Ten
Strategies to
remedy imbalance

Step Eleven
Your stress-management strategy

PART 1

DIAGNOSIS
&
UNDERSTANDING

REVIEW &
CONSOLIDATION

STRATEGIES
&
TECHNIQUES

MANAGING
THE
BALANCE

concludes, therefore, with reference to other books that continue the self-development process.

Now is the time to start on the first step. May I wish you a future with an enhanced lifestyle and the capacity to enjoy and manage the many challenges awaiting you.

Part 1
Diagnosis and understanding

Step One:
Disposition and stress

An important first step in managing stress is to identify your disposition. Once you have completed this step you will know your appropriate stress level and your vulnerability to suffering from the negative effects of stress.

The stance you take in a situation is influenced by your disposition. This is defined as your usual 'temperament' or 'frame of mind'. Under excessive pressure you may remain calm, or you may become very tense.

Your disposition will influence your preferred stress level. If you are a very active person you may thrive on a high level of pressure. A person who worries will prefer a much lower stress level.

Disposition will also affect vulnerability, or the likelihood of suffering from the negative effects of excessive stress. If you are very ambitious you run the risk of pushing yourself too hard, unlike a more relaxed person who is far less vulnerable.

A straightforward analysis of disposition has been developed by American researchers. They identified two types of manager whom they designated Type A and Type B. The Type A manager they described as ambitious, competitive and time-driven, and far more likely to suffer a heart attack than his Type B colleague. The Type B manager they described as relaxed, unambitious and casual about time.

To fully understand the relationship between disposition and likely reactions to excessive stress a more elaborate approach is needed. I have developed a basic list of six recognizable types:

- the Ambitious Type
- the Calm Type
- the Conscientious Type
- the Nonassertive Type
- the Lively Type
- the Anxious Type.

In Step One I will define and describe the types, and refer to likely causes of stress, vulnerability to stress and preferred stress levels. When you have read the descriptions you will be required to identify the type which bears the closest resemblance to yourself.

Please note: the descriptions have been written in the third person. I have used the pronoun 'he', rather than 'he/she' to avoid the descriptions becoming clumsy. The descriptions apply equally to men and women.

Type 1: The Ambitious Type
Definition

A person with a strong desire for success or achievement.

Description

The Ambitious Type closely resembles the Type A manager. He is likely to be successful in his chosen career, driven by the need to succeed. Commitment to his career is likely to be high and he is likely to be active and energetic, seldom finding time to relax. He is not prepared to waste time and may become rather impatient if required to wait for anything or anyone.

Inevitably, Ambitious Types are very common in management positions. These jobs usually require an ambitious, energetic person to get things done.

When relating to other people he may tend to be aggressive and argumentative. He has a strong need to dominate others, possibly because of hidden insecurities. Personal relationships and home life take second place in his priorities. He may even cancel a holiday if work commitments are pressing.

Internal pressures and demands are likely to be high. The Ambitious Type tends to set high standards and drives himself to achieve them. Failure is hard to accept.

Overload and meeting tight, self-imposed deadlines are potential causes of stress for the Ambitious Type.

Possible signs of stress include: sleeplessness, high blood pressure, heavy smoking or drinking and heart problems.

Preferred stress level
High.

Vulnerability to the effects of stress
High.

Type 2: The Calm Type

Definition

A Calm Type is tranquil, placid and does not easily become disturbed, agitated or excited.

Description

The Calm Type closely resembles the Type B manager. He is likely to be patient and unworried, and unlikely to set too many impossible objectives for himself.

He probably allows time to think and reflect over past achievements, unlike the Ambitious Type who is always striving to achieve goals. However, he is likely to achieve less than his more ambitious colleague. He may have the capacity to appreciate people's good characteristics and is less likely to become obsessed by the inadequacies of others. This approach enhances his self-esteem.

In relationships with others the Calm Type is usually able to give and receive affection and praise. He need not play a dominant role and is seldom irritated by others.

He probably keeps a balance between work and home. He is more able to devote time to leisure pursuits. Inner tensions are likely to remain low.

Other people, or stress carriers, are potential causes of stress.

Preferred stress level
Medium to low.

Vulnerability to the effects of stress
Low.

Type 3 – The Conscientious Type

Definition

A Conscientious Type is a person who is meticulous, taking great care over everything required of him.

Description

He is likely to be very reliable, single-minded, but may be stubborn. In his desire to do things thoroughly he can become obsessional.

The Conscientious Type may become over-concerned with getting things right, paying too much attention to detail and thus losing sight of longer term objectives.

Wanting to get the job done properly he probably prefers a set routine and is less able to manage change than the Calm or Ambitious Types. He may feel thrown off balance when something unexpected happens. He is less likely to seek challenge in his life, preferring the security associated with working within his range of competence.

As a manager the Conscientious Type is likely to believe in authority and tradition. This will influence the way in which he interacts with superiors and subordinates, giving a high degree of respect to his superiors, but expecting the same treatment from his subordinates.

Home life is likely to be equally organized. He may like to follow routines quite rigidly.

There may be a degree of inner tension and turmoil, particularly if the Conscientious Type feels he is losing control.

Other people, particularly those who fail to plan ahead, can cause the Conscientious Type stress, as can an excessive workload.

Preferred stress level
Low to moderate.

Vulnerability to the effects of stress
Moderate, high at times of change.

Type 4: The Nonassertive Type

Definition

A Nonassertive Type is unable to assert himself; he has difficulty standing up for his own rights.

Description

The main concern of the Nonassertive Type is to please others, thus avoiding conflict. His fear of how others may react causes him to run away from situations rather than confront them.

To avoid conflict he may interact with others in such a way that people either misunderstand him or ignore his requests. Instead, they may take advantage of him.

The Nonassertive Type may have difficulty in saying 'no' to requests for help from others.

Relationships with others are likely to be problematic. This stems from his inability to express his own needs, his desire to please others and his fear of confrontation.

The Nonassertive Type may experience inner tensions. These develop from feelings of resentment that others are taking advantage of him. He may also experience frustration because of his inability to satisfy his own needs, since he feels compelled to accommodate the needs of others. These inner tensions are likely to be a major source of stress for the Nonassertive Type.

Preferred stress level
Moderately low.

Vulnerability to the effects of stress
Moderate.

Type 5: The Lively Type

Definition

A Lively Type is a person who is full of vigour and experiences mental and emotional intensity.

Description

The Lively Type is likely to live life to the full. Unlike the Ambitious Type, who is driven by achievement, he needs a varied and interesting life. His basic philosophy is that 'variety is the spice of life'.

The Lively Type thrives on change and may become bored if he has the same job for too long.

He probably needs a high level of stimulation and challenge, and thrives on the surge of energy which results from the flow of adrenaline.

In his desire for excitement and challenge he may take unnecessary risks, act impulsively and put himself under excessive pressure.

The Lively Type is likely to enjoy relating to other people. However, because of his need for a varied life, he may not stay in one place for long.

Inner tensions may develop if the Lively Type pushes himself too far. He may run the risk of burn-out.

Sources of stress for the Lively Type are likely to be routine work, lack of change and internal pressures.

Preferred stress level
High.

Vulnerability to the effects of stress
Low.
High if he exerts excessive pressure on himself.

Type 6: The Anxious Type

Definition

An Anxious Type is a person who is worried and tense because of possible misfortune.

Description

The Anxious Type worries a lot and finds it difficult to relax. He is obsessed with doing things right. He plans for every eventuality, but will inevitably fail. He tends to panic, and this is exacerbated when things go wrong.

The Anxious Type devotes a great deal of mental energy to focusing on the future. This is unconstructive, however, because a lot of time is spent worrying about what might happen, rather than attending to what is actually happening.

Typical of the Anxious Type is over-concern with other people's evaluations and judgements. Self-confidence and self-esteem are likely to be low. This interferes with relationships at work and at home.

Changing environments create considerable uncertainty, and Anxious Types react defensively rather than rising to the challenge.

The Anxious Type is likely to experience a high degree of internal pressure and turmoil, and will probably have fairly intense negative emotions, including feelings of self-doubt.

Life generally is likely to be stressful for the Anxious Type, but challenging work, change and uncertainty will probably be particularly stressful.

Signs that the Anxious Type is suffering from stress include the possibility of persistent headaches, an inability to think straight, a predisposition to become dependent on tranquillizers and a tendency to suffer from nervous exhaustion.

Preferred stress level
Low.

Vulnerability to the effects of stress
High.

Now that you have read the descriptions of the six types, complete the following exercise to help you identify the type which fits your disposition most closely, and then assess the implications for your preferred stress level and vulnerability to stress.

Exercise: Identifying your disposition

1 Rank the types in order of their resemblance to your disposition. You may need to re-read the descriptions to complete this task.

1. . . 3 . . . . . .

2. . . 4 . . . . .

3. . . 2 . . . . . .

4. . . 6 . . . . .

5. . . . . 5 . . . .

6. . . . . 1 . . . .

2 Study the three types most like you and write down the preferred stress levels for each type.

1. . . LOW . . . .

2. . . LOW - MOD . .

3. . . HIGH . . . .

Is there any difference in preferred stress levels for the three types? If there is a difference you will need to take account of this when you develop your personal strategy for managing stress.

3 Study the three types most like you and write down the vulnerability for each type.

1. . . HIGH . . .

2. . . MOD - HIGH . .

3. . . HIGH . . .

Do any of the types make you vulnerable to suffering from the negative effects of stress?

When you have completed this exercise move on to Step Two.

Step Two:
Assessing vulnerability to stress

During the interviews and research conducted while preparing this book, it became apparent that some managers thrived on stress, whereas others experienced the same pressures, but reacted with distress and ill-health. Step Two will help you assess your vulnerability and understand the factors which make you more or less vulnerable to suffering from excessive stress.

If you are vulnerable you are open to attack and likely to be wounded. The likelihood depends on several factors. Your resistance to stress is enhanced by your physical and emotional wellbeing and, at a deeper level, by the development of an understanding and acceptance of yourself. These will give you the fitness, energy and self-confidence necessary to withstand excessive stresses.

Compare your own body with a car. You are probably very careful to use the correct grade of fuel in your car. Do you pay as close attention to the food you eat? If dirt gets into the carburettor you immediately become aware of the effect. You need to become as sensitive to your own body and its limitations. How much alcohol can you safely drink without feeling ill the following day? Which foods disagree with you? You also know the capacity of your car and its maximum speed. You would never keep pushing the engine beyond its limits, but you may abuse your body, forcing it to keep going when it may need time to restore energy and recover. You probably have your car serviced regularly, but do you give yourself the same care and attention?

To be able to resist the effects of excessive negative stress you need to raise your threshold level, thus reducing your vulnerability. What makes you more or less vulnerable to stress? There are several factors which influence physical and psychological wellbeing, and the factors are interactive. Psychological factors, for example emotional problems, can have an effect on your physical state of health and will lower your resistance to stress-related illness. They will be discussed more fully later.

First, you need to assess your vulnerability to excessive stress by completing a short exercise.

Exercise: How vulnerable am I to stress?

Study each of the following questions and give each one a score on a scale between 3 and 1.

A score of 3 means you can say 'definitely yes' / 'always' to the statement, e.g. 'I spend time walking each day.' Full agreement with this statement would give a score of 3.

A score of 2 means you are uncertain about your response, or you are in between, e.g. 'I avoid drinking at lunchtimes.' If you occasionally drink at lunchtime you would give this statement a score of 2.

A score of 1 means you can say 'definitely no' / 'never' to the statement, e.g. if you never play sport you would give statement 35 a score of 1.

Some items, of necessity, are negative statements, e.g. 'I never work at weekends.' If you never work at weekends you would agree with the statement and give it a score of 3.

1 _2_ I eat the right food in the right quantities.

2 _3_ I avoid drinking at lunchtimes.

3 _1_ I exercise to the point of perspiration at least three times a week.

4 _2_ I have a network of friends and acquaintances.

5 _1_ I am contented with my sex life.

6 _3_ I have at least one hobby/interest I pursue regularly.

7 _3_ I never work during the weekends.

8 ___ I engage regularly in prayer or meditation.

9 ___ I limit my intake of coffee, tea and cola drinks to five cups a day.

10 ___ I enjoy a drink of alcohol rather than need a drink. .

11 ___ I exert moderate physical energy in my daily life.

12 ___ I give and receive affection regularly.

13 ___ I regularly achieve sexual satisfaction.

14 ___ I allow myself time to relax every day.

15 ___ I restrict myself to realistic workloads and never work to excess.

16 ___ I usually find solutions to my problems.

17 ___ I maintain the appropriate weight for my height.

18 ___ I never drink alcohol alone.

19 ___ I climb the stairs rather than use the lift.

20 ___ I am able to display emotions rather than allow negative feelings to build up inside me.

21 ___ I am seldom impotent/frigid.

22 ___ I get seven to eight hours sleep at least four nights a week.

23 ___ I never let work dominate my life.

24 ___ I believe in myself.

25 ___ I avoid adding too much salt to my food.

26 ___ I rarely have a drink of alcohol when I return home from work.

17 ___ I follow a regular programme of exercise.

28 ___ I have people who are close to me and with whom I can discuss intimate problems.

29 ___ I have a loving sexual relationship.

30 ___ I do something for fun at least once a week.

31 _2_ I avoid talking about work in social situations.

32 _1_ I have an inner feeling of tranquillity.

33 _2_ I eat regular meals each day and avoid frequent snacks.

34 _1_ I would describe myself as a moderate drinker of alcohol (an average of 0–3 drinks a day).

35 _2_ I participate in a sport each week.

36 _1_ I have colleagues at work who give me emotional support.

37 _1_ I enjoy a stable emotional relationship.

38 _2_ I am able to enjoy myself.

39 _2_ I never work in the evenings.

40 _1_ I feel I have a deep sense of belonging, of being a part of things.

41 _2_ I regularly drink mineral water.

42 _3_ I smoke fewer than five cigarettes a day, or do not smoke at all.

43 _1_ I spend time walking each day.

44 _3_ I would seek help from friends or obtain professional advice if necessary.

45 _1_ I seldom feel sexually frustrated.

46 _3_ I am able to spend time doing nothing.

47 _2_ My home life and work are equally important to me.

48 _2_ I have learnt to rise above stressful situations.

When you have completed the exercise transfer the score for each question into the appropriate space next to the question number and total up each of the eight categories.

Vulnerability profile

A	B	C	D	E	F	G	H
1 ^{2} –	2 ^{3} –	3 ^{1} –	4 ^{2} –	5 ^{1} –	6 ^{3} –	7 ^{3} –	8 ^{1} –
9 ^{3} –	10 ^{3} –	11 ^{1} –	12 ^{1} –	13 ^{1} –	14 ^{2} –	15 ^{2} –	16 ^{3} –
17 ^{3} –	18 ^{2} –	19 ^{3} –	20 ^{2} –	21 ^{3} –	22 ^{3} –	23 ^{2} –	24 ^{2} –
25 ^{2} –	26 ^{2} –	27 ^{3} –	28 ^{2} –	29 ^{1} –	30 ^{3} –	31 ^{2} –	32 ^{1} –
33 ^{2} –	34 ^{1} –	35 ^{2} –	36 ^{1} –	37 ^{1} –	38 ^{2} –	39 ^{2} –	40 ^{1} –
41 ^{2} –	42 ^{3} –	43 ^{1} –	44 ^{3} –	45 ^{1} –	46 ^{3} –	47 ^{2} –	48 ^{2} –

Totals

– – – – – – – –

A – Healthy diet   14
B – Avoiding alcoholism and smoking   14
* C – Programme of exercise   11
D – Emotional wellbeing   13
* E – Fulfilling sex life   8
F – Relaxation and enjoyment ·   16
G – Balance between home and work   13
* H – Self-understanding and acceptance   10

Interpreting your scores

The purpose of this exercise is to help you diagnose some of the factors which may make you more or less resistant to stress. It is a subjective measure, but managers completing this exercise found it helped them to reflect on the extent to which they took care of their physical and psychological wellbeing.

The eight factors selected are those which health experts and psychologists commonly agree to be an influence on vulnerability to stress. You are able to score a maximum of 18 and a minimum of 6 for any one factor.

A score of 15 or more. First ask yourself the question 'Have I been really honest when I answered the questions?' Some managers admitted that their scores reflected the situation they would like to exist, rather than reality. If your scores are genuine then that particular factor is unlikely to make you vulnerable. If you score 15 or more for all the factors then you are more likely to be able to withstand stress than the person with much lower scores.

A score between 10 and 14. You are not particularly vulnerable to stress at the moment, but as your score is a little on the low side it should monitored.

A score of 9 or less. You are more likely to suffer the effects of stress. If you obtained any low scores look back over the questions and establish the reasons. The next part describes the factors associated with vulnerability. When you have read that part you may decide to make certain changes to your life.

Factors affecting vulnerability

A review of this section will help you to reflect on the need for life changes. Step Ten will help you consolidate the changes into a plan of action.

A Healthy diet

Nutrition is a subject in its own right. This section will merely help you to assess whether your diet is adequate. Eating a well-balanced diet helps your body to operate efficiently and provides you with the energy needed to maintain a good state of health.

What to eat

You need a balance of fresh food, including protein – particularly white meat and fish – a small amount of fat, limited carbohydrate and plenty of fresh fruit and vegetables. Nutrition experts also recommend a high level of fibre in your diet.

Vitamin tablets may also help you, particularly when you are under severe pressure. Vitamins B and C are useful supplements in these situations. Vitamin B affects mental attitude and helps you cope with stress. Vitamin C helps you to resist the harmful effects of stress.

Experts also believe you can have too much of certain foods. You should avoid too much red meat, excessive fat, and try to restrict your sugar intake. Excessive salt can cause high blood pressure and, ultimately, heart disease and strokes.

Action

If you are concerned about the quality of your diet you might like to read a book on the subject. References are on page 158.

Review your diet and assess whether you need to make any changes.

B Alcoholism and smoking

Alcoholism

A small amount of alcohol probably enhances your wellbeing and helps you relax. Alcohol in excess is very damaging to your health and impairs work performance. Excessive drinking, particularly of spirits, increases the risk of suffering from cirrhosis of the liver. You are less likely to make effective decisions, achieve clarity of thought, and your judgement may become impaired. The executive is greatly at risk from excessive drinking, with the danger of ultimately becoming an alcoholic. Drinking is not an effective strategy for managing stress.

Cigarette smoking

An occasional cigarette helps you to relax and to concentrate. However, cigarettes quickly become addictive. The more you smoke, the greater the health risk. There is a known correlation between smoking and lung cancer, cardiovascular disease and bronchitis. As with drinking, there is a tendency to smoke more when you feel stressed.

If you are a smoker, become aware of what it does to you. Cigarettes contain three active ingredients: nicotine, tar and carbon monoxide. When you inhale, nicotine is taken into the lungs and stimulates both the respiratory tract and the brain. People sometimes smoke to increase concentration. Nicotine also has negative effects. It narrows the coronary arteries and raises blood pressure and cholesterol levels. Tar builds up in the lungs, resulting in bronchitis and lung cancer.

Action

If you had a low score, review your drinking and smoking habits. Is this a factor that requires changes to be made?

C Programme of exercise

While following a planned programme of exercise you are far more likely to dissipate the harmful effects of stress by burning off adrenaline and preventing the build-up of cholesterol in the arteries. You are likely to acquire the stamina to withstand the demands made upon you at work, and exercise will help release tension which has built up in your body. You are less likely to suffer from fatigue and depression.

Action

If you have a low score, consider adopting a strategy in Step Ten that will help develop your physical stamina.

D Emotional wellbeing

This factor can be subdivided into three components which will be considered separately:

- Emotional support.
- Ability to display emotions.
- Opportunity to give and receive affection.

Emotional support

'A problem shared is a problem halved' is a popular saying. If you have people you can turn to and with whom you can discuss intimate problems, the situation is less likely to grow out of all proportion in your mind.

While a self-reliant, independent approach to life is desirable and necessary for managers, there are times when you may need support from others to help you through a difficult time at work or at home. You may receive this support from your spouse, relatives, friends or colleagues.

Action

Review your support network and decide whether or not it is adequate.

Also, assess whether you are able to take full advantage of your support network. Several of the managers interviewed indicated that they found difficulty in talking to others about personal problems.

Ability to display emotions

Most people experience emotional reactions to situations at work and at home, but vary in their capacity to display these emotions. If someone annoys you at work do you let them know you are annoyed or do you bottle it up inside?

In certain cultures upbringing encourages the stiff-upper-lip approach to life. From an early age children may be conditioned to control emotions, receiving messages such as 'don't cry', 'be brave' and 'don't get angry'. A certain degree of control is necessary, but the healthy person is able to show his feelings and avoid the tension of negative emotions turned inwards.

The ability to display emotions helps you to develop a more positive approach to life. If you allow negative feelings to build up you become frustrated or depressed. Display positive feelings and people are likely to reciprocate these positive feelings, enhancing your sense of wellbeing.

Action

Spend time reflecting, and decide whether you are able to display feelings in the appropriate way. There will be a strategy in Step Ten to help those who need to manage their emotions more effectively.

Opportunity to give and receive affection

Some psychologists believe that people strive for recognition from others. Research conducted in children's homes in the United States showed that the physical needs of children were well taken care of, but emotionally they were often deprived. Children need the recognition which can be derived from close relationships with parents. They thrive in situations where they receive a lot of physical contact, as well as verbal recognition.

People's physical wellbeing is enhanced by the opportunity to give affection. For example, medical evidence has shown that some patients recovering from open heart surgery recover more quickly if they have a pet they can stroke. The opportunity to take care of emotional needs helps physical wellbeing.

You may be aware that people vary in the amount of affection they need to give and receive. If you were deprived of affection as a child you may settle for less affection as an adult, or you may spend the rest of your life trying to make up the deficit.

Action

Insufficient opportunity to give and receive affection will create tension in your life. Think of the opportunities available to you: is the balance satisfactory, or do you need to make any changes to your life?

E Fulfilling sex life

This is a highly effective and enjoyable way to release tension and make you more able to withstand stress. The sexual act alone, particularly when an orgasm is achieved, enhances physical wellbeing. The benefits are much greater when sex forms a part of a deep emotional relationship. In this situation possibly as many as four of the factors under discussion are satisfied.

Action

At this stage you need to ask yourself whether your sex life is sufficiently satisfying. Are you falling into the trap of allowing work to dominate, leaving yourself with a lack of energy for sex? If you become overstressed a symptom is a loss of interest in sex. Does this apply to you? If so, perhaps changes in your life are necessary.

F Relaxation and enjoyment

All work and no play makes Jack a dull boy, and vulnerable to excessive stress! You need balance in your life. For the successful manager this means a hobby or interest that provides the opportunity to unwind. The manager who no longer finds his job demanding – the plateaued manager – may need to find stimulation outside work. This may be found in local government, or through undertaking voluntary work.

Without the opportunity to switch off from work, the likelihood that you will suffer from stress becomes much greater. The key question you must ask yourself is, 'Do I have fun in my life?'

You also need to assess whether you allow yourself time for complete rest and relaxation. Are there times in the week when you do very little? Do you ensure that you have enough sleep at night? Rest is essential for remaining in a good state of health. Many managers live their life on a knife-edge, close to burn-out and collapse.

One of the best forms of relaxation is a holiday. This provides the chance to get away from the everyday routine at work and at home. You could view a holiday as a form of investment in your future. You do need to plan the holiday carefully, matching the choice with your ability to unwind. You also need to allow time for readjustment when you return to work.

Several of the managers interviewed failed to take their full holiday allowance. They had reached a stage of feeling indispensible, and had lost sight of the benefits of a holiday.

Action

Think back over the last few years and ask yourself whether you have allowed yourself sufficient time for relaxation and rest. If not, you may be operating close to exhaustion, and you are most unlikely to be performing at peak efficiency. Techniques to help relaxation have been included in Step Ten.

G Balance between home and work

Many of you may feel the balance between home and work is inappropriate. In the Victorian age a favourite saying was 'The devil finds work for idle hands to do.' While this is less of a driving force today, the saying still holds true for many managers. Those of you who are engaged in interesting, rewarding work can probably work extended hours, with a high level of commitment, without personal sacrifice. You are able to thrive on work and able to work hard and play hard, thus maintaining the appropriate balance in your life.

Those of you who perhaps find your work frustrating, boring or unsuccessful may fall into the trap of becoming obsessed with work. Unfortunately, if this happens to you, the harder you work the more inefficient you become and you find yourself working even harder to compensate for the inefficiency.

Action

Take a cold, hard look at yourself: are you in danger of becoming a workaholic? Are you always working, or thinking about work, even when you are at home?

H Understanding and acceptance of self

If you understand yourself, your needs and motives, and accept yourself and your limitations, you are more likely to reach a feeling of inner peace. This enables you to accept the stress you experience and helps you to keep situations in perspective.

There are a number of techniques you can practise that will help you achieve a feeling of inner peace. The techniques include meditation, relaxation and self-healing. These are particularly helpful in reducing the impact of stress because they slow the body down and reverse the stress reaction.

People who regularly practise relaxation and meditation report a number of beneficial effects. For example, these techniques can help to lower your blood pressure. Most people say their self-esteem is increased and they feel calmer and more able to withstand the effects of stress. They also feel it broadens their perspective on life and they feel more in control of their destinies.

Action

Do you strive for a deeper feeling of peace and tranquillity? If this is the case you may like to consider one of the techniques mentioned. These will be discussed further in Step Ten.

Now that you have had a chance to assess your vulnerability to stress, and reflected on the factors associated with it, complete Step Two by filling in the Vulnerability Review. You can then move on to the next step.

Vulnerability review

For each of the vulnerability factors summarize how well you are observing that factor.

A Healthy diet

B Alcoholism and smoking

C Programme of exercise

D Emotional wellbeing

E Fulfilling sex life

F Relaxation and enjoyment

G Balance between home and work

H Understanding and acceptance of self

Step Three:
Understanding stress

Having assessed the factors influencing vulnerability to stress, the next step will develop your understanding of stress. By the end of Step Three you should know what happens to your body and mind when you are exposed to a threatening situation or excessive pressure. You will also become aware of the interactive nature of stress between yourself and your environment, and the importance of your perception of the situation in determining your reaction to it.

The manager's view of stress

Stress means different things to different people. In the survey managers were asked:
'What do you mean by the term stress?'
How would you answer this question?
   Pause for a moment and decide what response you would make.
   The most common replies included:

- too much work and too little time to do it
- a feeling of anxiety
- being unable to cope
- too much pressure
- feeling tired and irritable
- emotional pressure.

Two interesting points emerge:

1 There were two types of answers:

- those related to the causes of stress
- those related to the effects of stress.

From here onwards the causes of stress, or *stressors*, will be differentiated from the effects of stress, or *symptoms of stress*.

2 Most people seem to view stress in a fairly negative way.

This does not have to be the case. Pressure can be seen as positive, because it provides you with extra energy to meet demands from outside or those which are self-imposed. Some managers described stress as a feeling of elation and being able to rise to a challenge. You can probably think of a situation you have experienced where you surprised yourself at the performance you achieved. This will be discussed more fully later in this step.

Having been given a brief explanation of stress, the managers interviewed then gave a much more detailed description of what stress meant to them. Two of these responses are described below, to demonstrate the different ways managers can experience stress.

Joe was a quiet, meticulous person working as an electronics engineer in a large, high-technology establishment. He felt very able to keep on top of the technical aspects of his job. He knew what he was doing and felt in control. A year ago he was promoted to the position of team leader of an important project. Faced with the task of managing a group of junior engineers he felt very inadequate and described the situation as stressful. Questioned further he explained that he found delegation difficult and was unused to motivating others. He also experienced pressure from the problem of relating to his team. As time progressed he felt tense and regularly suffered from headaches. Joe saw stress as having a damaging effect on work performance.

Joe's response to stress was negative. He assessed himself as inadequate to cope with the situation facing him and tension built up inside him. Eventually he suffered from headaches and his work performance deteriorated.

Joe's case may be typical of some people who are given managerial responsibilities. Perhaps you can identify with him. Most feel confident technically but find the task of managing people more difficult. Supervising staff is a known source of stress. Frequently, people are promoted because they have the greater technical expertise, but can be the least suited managerially. Organizations sometimes fail to supply the necessary training for managers to help them fulfil their roles effectively.

Duncan viewed stress rather differently. He was employed as a marketing manager for a large pharmaceutical company. His job required him to travel, meet a wide range of people and make presentations to large groups. He was an outgoing person, found his job challenging and thrived on the pressure derived from his job.

He associated stress with making a presentation to a large group of people. Have you ever been asked to do this? If so, you can probably remember the sensation you felt as you stood up in front of the audience. Duncan described it as a rush of energy firing his body, making his heart beat faster, and focusing his mind sharply. This reaction helped him to give a lively and dynamic performance.

These case histories illustrate the different perceptions people have of stress. It does not have to be seen as negative. Some people thrive on stress, depending on their dispositions, which were identified in the first step. One secret of stress management is to adopt a positive attitude to stress (like Duncan). The extra energy, generated as a result of imbalance, can then be channelled towards achieving an enhanced performance. Negative outcomes can thus be avoided. This will be explained more fully in Step Eight.

Having described stress from the viewpoint of managers, the next step, in order to understand stress more fully, is to explore the views of experts.

A study of research shows that stress can basically be described in one of three ways:

1 As an *external factor* or *stimulus* exerting a force on the person – the **stimulus** approach.

2 As a *response* or *reaction* to an external factor – the **response** approach.

3 As a reaction resulting from an *imbalance* between the external and internal demands on the person and his or her perceived capability for meeting those demands – the **interactional** approach.

I have adopted the third way of describing stress, but all three approaches, starting with the stimulus approach, will be discussed further to help you better understand stress.

The stimulus approach

The stimulus view of stress is the one often used by the layperson. The *Oxford Dictionary* definition of 'stress' is 'pressure', which is a stimulus view.

Engineers also use this meaning of the word when they calculate the stress a building must withstand. Their view is that a building has to be able to cope with certain stresses – the load or demand placed upon it. The response to the stress is strain. If the building is subjected to excessive stress, then permanent damage will result. This is shown in Figure 2.

```
        Stress ——▶ Strain
    External force


Excessive stress ——▶ Collapse/Permanent damage
```

Figure 2 **Stimulus approach to stress**

People are also able to withstand certain pressures, but the level of resistance varies. Some cope with excessive pressure in their lives, while others collapse very quickly. You assessed your vulnerability in the previous step. Predictions can be made more easily about the impact of pressure on buildings than they can about the impact on people.

Some researchers have developed this approach further, stating that stress arises when the level of demand on the person departs from optimum conditions. For example, there is an optimum temperature at which you feel comfortable to work. You become stressed if you are too hot or too cold. This makes the point that being too cold is as bad as being too hot. Similarly, a lack of work, or undemanding work, affects you just as much as too much work.

External factors will be referred to as *stressors*. You must become aware of the stressors in your life in order to manage stress successfully. You will be given the opportunity to do this in a later step. You will then have a clearer picture of what triggers the next reaction, the stress *response*.

The response approach

People who adopt a response-based approach focus on the reactions of the individual to environmental demands. The response may be physiological – for example, your heart beats faster – or psychological – you feel irritable. This is shown in Figure 3.

Figure 3 **The response approach**

The response approach was adopted by Dr Hans Selye, an Austrian-born physician. He experimented with animals and found that whatever demands were placed on the animal, such as extremes of temperature or a threatening situation, the reaction was the same. He called this reaction the *general adaptation syndrome*, and believed an identical syndrome was experienced by people.

This approach provides a useful starting point for understanding stress, but it probably rather over-simplifies the complex nature of the subject. Today, researchers believe that responses may vary from situation to situation. This has led to a third view of stress developing: the interactional approach.

The interactional approach

This approach takes the understanding of stress a stage further by intensively studying the interaction between the individual and his environment. Up until recently, people have been understood to take a relatively passive role, reacting fairly automatically to situations.

Now, however, researchers have realized that people behave more interactively; they weigh up the demands of a situation against their appraisal of their own capacity for meeting those demands. This approach regards stress as resulting from an imbalance between the level of demand placed on the individual, as he sees it, and his perceived capability for meeting those demands. This is shown in Figure 4 and is more easily understood by considering an example.

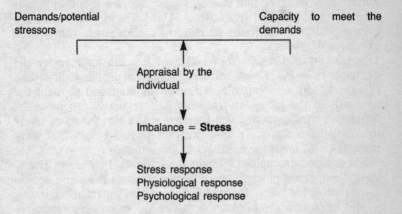

Figure 4 **The interactional approach**

Most of you probably need secretaries in your work. The next case was described by a manager and is a good illustration of the components of stress.

Margaret, Jill and Fiona were three secretaries, each of whom experienced stress for different reasons. Margaret was a very capable secretary who seemed to thrive on pressure. She provided secretarial support for several managers and she always seemed to be on top of her work. The managers could always rely on Margaret to meet really tight deadlines. Then two new managers joined the department and Margaret was also expected to provide secretarial support for them. Up until that time Margaret had experienced a balance between demands and her capacity to meet those demands. The extra demands placed upon Margaret were such that she suddenly felt unable to cope. Her work output fell dramatically and she failed to meet deadlines. She was suffering from stress and her work performance had deteriorated as a result.

You may also experience stress because you feel you lack the capacity to meet the demands put upon you. Jill became stressed for this reason. She was a lively girl who had been promoted to the position of personal secretary more on the grounds of personality than for her secretarial skills. She had difficulty establishing priorities and was unhappy when left to work on her own initiative. Whenever her manager gave her work without clear guidance she suffered from stress. Unlike Margaret it was her own capabilities which she percieved as inadequate, rather than excessive demands.

Stress can also result from a lack of stamina for meeting the demands of work. Fiona suffered from this problem. She, like Margaret, was very capable and normally managed to meet the demands of the job. Unfortunately, she regularly caught colds. Whenever this happened she found that she was far more likely to suffer from stress. In this case her physical resources were inadequate to meet the demands of the situation.

These three examples highlight the individual nature of stress. Everyone perceives situations differently. Even the same person can perceive the same situation differently on separate occasions.

The interactional approach provides the most comprehensive view of stress and has useful implications for stress management. Accordingly this is the approach used throughout this book. The definition of stress is as follows:

Stress is the physiological and psychological reaction that occurs when people perceive an imbalance between the level of demand placed upon them and their capability for meeting that demand.

Although stress is defined as an imbalance, this may be either positive or negative. Your body and mind respond to this imbalance, which is experienced as additional energy or damaging distress. A constructive response to these sensations will drive you to restore the balance and adopt an effective coping strategy.

The coping strategy you adopt to try to restore the balance may be successful or unsuccessful. If you adopt a successful coping strategy, for example reducing the demands on you, then your stress level will fall. If your strategy fails – for example you ignore the problem, hoping it will go away – the problem will be exacerbated and you will experience stress even more acutely. The change in the degree of stress you experience comes about when you reappraise the situation by weighing up the balance between demands and capacity.

The cyclical nature of stress can be understood by looking further at the case of Margaret. She experienced stress when extra demands were made upon her. She had at least two possible alternatives. She could, for example, try to work faster to complete the additional work. This could well result in her feeling totally exhausted – an unsuccessful coping strategy. On reappraising the situation she would probably see an even greater imbalance between demands and her capacity for meeting them. Alternatively, she could confront her boss and suggest the workload was too great. Some of the work being reallocated to other secretaries would be a more effective way of handling the situation. It should reduce her stress level – provided she asserts herself, rather than feeling guilty for refusing to undertake the additional workload. Strategies for coping with stress will be discussed more fully in Steps Eight, Nine and Ten.

You should now have a clearer picture of what is meant by the term 'stress'. Before completing Step Three you need to know more about your response to stress in physiological and psychological terms.

The physiological reaction: understanding your body chemistry

When you react to a threatening situation, several changes take place in your body. You are probably familiar with the feelings you experience when you narrowly miss having a car accident, are about to sit an examination, or become exposed to any frightening situation. The way you feel is the result of a number of physiological changes taking place in your body. These changes are described in more detail below and the sequence is shown as a flow diagram in Figure 5.

1 When you are faced with a threatening situation chemical messages in the brain are carried along tracks – called neurons – to the hypothalamus. This is situated in the lower part of the brain. It is very sensitive to the effects of drugs, stress and intense

Figure 5 **The chemistry of stress**

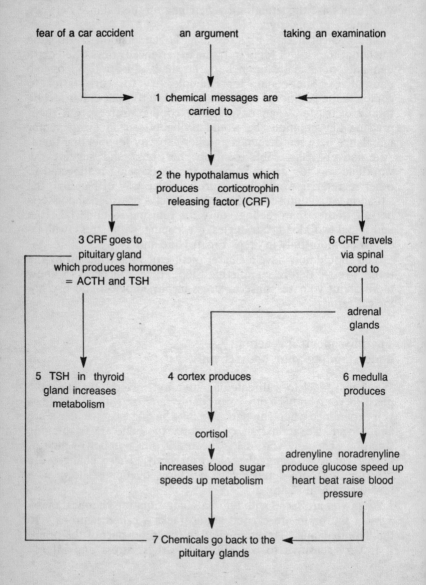

emotion and is largely responsible for changes in appetite, weight, water-balance and mood.

2 The hypothalamus produces a chemical called corticotrophin (CRF). This, along with other chemicals, goes to the pituitary gland and the centre – or the medulla – of the adrenal glands.

3 The pituitary gland, by controlling the flow of hormones from other glands, plays an important part in reactions to stress. It produces the adrenocorticotropic hormone (ACTH) and a thyroid stimulating hormone (TSH).

4 ACTH travels to the outer layer – or cortex – of the adrenal glands. The adrenal glands are two small glands lying close to the kidneys. The chemical cortisol is produced in the cortex. This increases the level of sugar in the blood and speeds up the metabolism of the body.

5 TSH travels to the thyroid gland at the front of the neck. This controls energy levels – increased energy results from an increase in metabolic rate.

6 Meanwhile CRF and other chemicals travel from the hypothalamus along the spinal cord to the middle, or medulla, of the adrenal glands. Chemical reactions take place in the medulla and hormones are produced. These are called adrenaline and noradrenaline, and are secreted into the bloodstream. This produces a response sometimes referred to as the 'fight or flight response'. This response will be discussed more fully below.

7 Chemicals are then fed back from the medulla and cortex of the adrenal glands to the pituitary gland. This continues to control the stress response.

The effect of the chemicals and hormones on your body helps to explain why you experience particular symptoms when you suffer from stress. These can act as warning signs and early diagnosis is important to avoid harmful effects building up. The symptoms will be discussed fully in Step Six.

Ian, a civil engineer, gave a good illustration of the stress response when he described the start of a typical day.

He woke up with the alarm ringing and remembered he needed

to be at work early that day. He jumped out of bed, showered, shaved, swallowed a quick cup of tea and ran out to the car. Within minutes he was stuck in rush-hour traffic. Would he make his first appointment he asked himself? Already Ian could feel the pressure mounting. He arrived at work with only seconds to spare. The doors closed as he reached the lift, but Ian decided to wait rather than walk up five flights of stairs. He entered his office; his boss arrived immediately and started to criticize the report Ian had submitted a week before. Ian felt the urge to strike him. Instead he sat down at his desk. His boss left and Ian looked at the pile of papers in his in-tray. He sat, reflecting on the boss's comments, and felt his neck muscles tighten and his stomach churn.

You can probably understand what has been happening to Ian. The chemical changes necessary to make him get out of bed have built up more and more as the morning has progressed. Without much physical activity the detrimental effects are able to build up. Ian would have felt much better if he had walked up the stairs rather than wait for the lift. This would have reduced the level of tension. Note the urge to be aggressive when Ian's boss criticized him. Instead, Ian kept the feelings to himself and he experienced tension in the neck and the stomach. He may have reduced the tension if he had confronted his boss, or hit him!

'The fight or flight response'

Adrenaline and noradrenaline make the body rev up for action, rather like an aeroplane before take off. This is one of our most primitive responses, and it was obviously essential for the cave-man's survival. It gave him the energy he needed to cope with dangerous animals. Today, you seldom need to be physically active, and sometimes these hormones can accumulate in your body, leaving you feeling frustrated, irritable and impatient.

Reflect for a moment – can you recall a situation which has triggered this fight or flight response?

Sue Lawley, in a recent television interview, was asked if anyone had ever angered her on television. She replied, 'Yes. I am afraid I have to say this – Arthur Scargill, when I was inter-viewing him during the miners' strike.' She then went on to give an amusing account of what actually happened. As the interview developed she grew angry when he expressed unpopular views and felt a surge of energy flow through her body. Unfortunately, she had a microphone clipped inside her dress. She then had a very disturbed technical director on her hands because her heart was beating so violently that it muffled the conversation being held. All that could be heard was her racing heart!

This provides a good example of the body revving up for action, but adrenaline and noradrenaline also have other effects. In particular they influence how alert you feel. Adrenaline seems to focus concentration and helps to improve memory. Too low a level of noradrenaline causes depression. Exercise, such as swimming, running or dancing, raises the level of noradrenaline and helps to lift depression.

What other physiological changes occur in your body during stressful times?

The body retains fluid

When you are worried or anxious the pituitary glands secrete an antidiuretic hormone that encourages the tissues to hold water. Have you ever experienced that bloated feeling when you are worrying about something? Now you know the reason why.

Prolonged stress

So far the discussion has concentrated on the immediate reaction to a perceived threat. But what happens over longer periods of time? Gradually the adrenal glands become exhausted through overwork and cease to operate efficiently. You are then likely to feel over tired, your muscles feel weak and you have difficulty getting to sleep and waking up. You are likely to develop a craving for sweet, starchy foods, have difficulty with digestion and may feel dizzy. These and other symptoms will be discussed further in Step Six.

You should by now have a fairly thorough understanding of the way your body responds to stress, but this is only a part of the picture. The underlying assumption so far has been that reaction to the external environment is purely physiological. However, people also respond psychologically to stress and experience a range of emotions.

The psychological reaction: understanding your emotions

The psychological impact of potential stressors on the individual should not be overlooked. The 'fight/flight' response has been extended to include the response of 'freezing'. This response is often observed in cats when they are faced with danger, but can also occur in humans, as the following case history demonstrates.

Richard, a test pilot, was testing a small aircraft with just an instructor on board. He had put the plane through its paces and was making one last difficult turn before returning to the airfield. At this moment the engine stalled and the aircraft started to lose height. Richard described his reaction as one of 'freezing'. He sat in the seat, totally immobile, experiencing blind panic. He then realized that to stay alive he had to react. He collected himself and landed the plane safely in a field. His instructor, to prevent a recurrence, later trained him to control tension. Richard is now a far more relaxed person.

This example shows how the individual interprets the situation in which he finds himself. In this case fear was the dominant emotion, and it influenced the way Richard's body reacted. Stress is not purely a physiological response, but is the outcome of the interaction between the individual and his environment.

The interactive approach provides the best view of stress. It emphasizes the importance of the individual's appraisal of his situation. For this reason, strategies for managing stress will also vary from person to person, depending on the appraisal.

You will be able to manage stress far more effectively if you are able to keep the right balance between outer demands and your inner resources for meeting those demands. What are the demands in your life at present? Step Four will help to identify these factors.

Step Four:
Diagnosing the causes of stress

Everyone experiences excessive pressure at some time or other. For some of us 'overload' is virtually continuous. Not all pressure is negative. It may be linked with something pleasurable, for example the stimulation of promotion, or the excitement of a new job. Alternatively, the pressure may cause overload and distress. This may be provoked by being passed over for promotion, or losing a job.

Your reactions to pressure are very personall; they may or may not give rise to stress, depending on your assessment of the situation. Pressure can be viewed as beneficial or harmful; as a challenge or as a threat. You need to understand the reasons for this in more detail.

The purpose of Step Four is to help you identify the pressures that currently exist in your life, whether at home or at work, that cause you distress. The pressures examineed in this step should be differentiated from 'life events', which will be looked at in Step Five and used to assess your current stress level. Life events may be positive or negative – they represent some form of *change* in your life.

Now complete the exercise 'What causes you stress?'

Exercise: What causes you stress?

This exercise has been designed in the form of a checklist to help you recognize current causes of stress. These may change periodically so you may need to repeat this exercise from time to time when stress recurs.

The checklist has been broken down into six major areas which are further subdivided into factors. The factors included in the checklist were those most frequently mentioned by managers in the survey.

Study each statement and rate it from 4 to 0 as follows:

A score of 4 means it is highly likely to cause you stress.
A score of 3 means it is quite likely to cause you stress.
A score of 2 means 'in between'/'don't know'.
A score of 1 means it is fairly unlikely to cause you stress.
A score of 0 means it is very unlikely to cause you stress.

Place your score in the space provided.

1 Organization. The organization in which I work evokes negative stress because:

a____of frustration resulting from 'red tape';
b____there are constant changes in the organization;
c____the organization operates at a fast pace to keep ahead of competitors;
d____the organization operates in a customer-orientated environment.

2 Job. The job I currently undertake is stressful because:

a____the amount of work is inappropriate (either too much or too little);
b____I am required to take frequent decisions;
c____I frequently need to meet deadlines;
d____I am required to manage others or take responsibility for the lives of others.

3 Career. My current career causes me stress because:

a____I feel my needs are not being met;
b____I lack clear goals;
c____I have reached the ceiling in my present job;
d____I lack the ability to do the job.

4 Relationships. Relationships create stress in my life, in particular those with:

a____superiors;
b____subordinates;
c____colleagues;
d____family and/or friends.

5 Outside work. Family pressures cause me stress, in particular:

a____I experience conflict between work and home demands;
b____I have excessive demands from immediate family/relatives;
c____I have difficulty meeting my financial commitments.

6 Internal stressors. I feel I experience stress which is self-generated because:

a____I set unrealistically high standards and goals for myself;
b____I fear appearing foolish or incompetent to others or am driven by a fear of failure;
c____I have a negative view of myself which generates tension;
d____I have certain needs within me which remain unsatisfied;
e____I seem unable to manage myself and my time and/or fail to attend to my wellbeing.

Now transfer your scores to the summary table.

Summary Table: Causes of Stress

1 Organization   **2** Job
a____   a____
b____   b____
c____   c____
d____   d____

3 Career   **4** Relationships
a____   a____
b____   b____
c____   c____
d____   d____

5 Outside work   **6** Internal stressors
a____   a____
b____   b____
c____   c____
                                 d____
                                 e____

Review the summary sheet and identify the five most damaging stressors which are affecting you now. List them below.

1 . . .
2 . . .
3 . . .
4 . . .
5 . . .

Read the appropriate description of the most damaging stressor to sharpen your understanding. Read the other descriptions if you are interested.

- Organization or employer, see pages 50–1.
- Job, see pages 51–4.
- Career, see pages 54–5.
- Relationships, sees page 55–6.
- Outside work, sees page 56–7.
- Internal stressors, see pages 57–61.

What are the stressors in your life?

1 *From your organization or employer*

Having interviewed managers from a range of organizations I have come to the conclusion that some organizations are potentially more stressful than others. The degree of pressure generated depends on a number of factors:

(a) Amount of red tape

Many people gave examples of red tape or bureaucracy as sources of stress. This is closely associated with large organizations, particularly in the public sector.

(b) Changes in the organization

For example, the UK health service has undergone dramatic changes. This has created the need for a change in the structure of jobs. Some jobs have disappeard and some staff have had to reapply for their own, or slightly different, jobs. The people involved described the changes as highly stressful.

(c) High technology

Those of you who are involved in high-technology organizations, such as the computer industry, will have known people who worked until they could give no more – a phenomenon known as burn-out. This happens when employees fight to help the company maintain its market share by keeping up to date with rapidly advancing technology.

(d) Service industry

Some of you may have to manage in a customer-orientated environment. You will be able to identify with the demands made upon you by customers. Jobs in this sector involve extensive contact with people, and you are often expected to handle difficult situations. The people with whom you interact are often themselves suffering from stress. For example, in the travel industry customers may suffer from stress particularly if they are not seasoned travellers.

2 From your job

The job itself

Certain occupations are potentially more stressful than others. If you work in the caring professions, for example as a doctor, nurse or social worker, you may find yourself continually giving emotional support to others. Unless you are able to restore the balance and in turn receive support yourself your job can become a source of stress. The Samaritans, a UK organization for helping distressed people, are very aware of this problem and train their volunteers never to leave a spell of duty without first receiving some support from another volunteer.

Providing a service to other functions can also become stressful. The data processing manager of an engineering company was interviewed and gave the following explanation.

Neville was data processing manager for a medium-sized engineering company. He chain-smoked throughout the interview as he related the pressures of his job. He complained of work overload, machine breakdown, shortage of staff, and the difficulty of managing a situation which was sometimes outside his direct control. He also talked of the stresses of being the man in the middle – between the computer and the users – trying hard to keep everyone happy. He described times when he worked day and night to get systems up and running successfully.

Those of you working in the data processing field may well be able to identify with Neville. What are the characteristics of your job which make it stressful? Managers in the survey identified:

(a) Amount of work

There is an optimum level of work you are able to undertake without becoming stressed. This factor was the one most commonly mentioned by the managers in the survey. Too much work and you experience what is called *overload*, too little work and you experience what is referred to as *underload* – this creates stress through apathy or boredom.

Underload is possibly more likely to be stressful than overload. Research conducted in the 1970s showed that more people suffered from stress-related illnesses at shop floor level, employed in routine work, than at executive or manager level.

People may react to the stress of routine work by becoming apathetic or frustrated, as the cases of Andrew and Paul demonstrate.

Andrew was an intelligent man, but lacked clear goals. At the age of twenty-three he found himself in a routine clerical position, his abilities under-utilized. He described himself as feeling apathetic and bored, and finally felt reluctant to get out of bed in the morning. By contrast, Paul, who was working as a management trainee, felt extremely frustrated when his traineeship failed to provide him with sufficient scope to develop managerial skills. He experienced feelings of tension, and reacted in a much more explosive way.

Your current job may be stressful because of underload or overload. Overload can take different forms. It may result from too much work being allocated to you, or attracting too much work to yourself. It may also exist because the work is too difficult for you, or beyond your capabilities.

Your assessment of your workload is highly subjective and will vary. Sometimes you will feel able to undertake large amounts of work. At other times smaller amounts become a burden. This is partly a reflection of mental attitude. Perhaps Blanchard has the solution, writing in *Leadership and the One Minute Manager* (see Further Reading, page 158). He says 'work smarter not harder'. You may suffer from overload because you are working ineffectively.

(b) Decision-making

An important aspect of the manager's job is the need to take decisions. The fear of making the wrong decision, which could be costly for the organization, may be a major source of stress for the senior manager.

At a more junior level many managers also fear the implications of making a wrong decision. When the decision-making process is viewed as a stressor, a common, but important, strategy for coping is to delay or avoid making a decision. Eventually a particular decision could be forced on the manager making him operate in a reactive way. The capacity to take decisions also deteriorates once a person becomes stressed. For this reason decision-making can be viewed as a source of stress, and poor decision-making as an effect of excessive stress.

(c) Meeting deadlines

Work which can be described as a series of peaks or troughs is far more stressful than work which operates at a steady pace. People employed in the publishing industry will be able to identify with the stress of working to tight deadlines. Are you driven by the need to achieve the deadline and find relaxation difficult until the deadline has been reached? Working with time constraints makes life highly stressful.

(d) Responsibility for people

Having responsibility for people may mean either managing others or actually having responsibility for their lives. In the first case demands are made upon you for managing relationships and coping with the needs of a group of people. In the latter case the pressure is even greater and might apply to an airline pilot, air traffic controller or a consultant surgeon. As one surgeon said during an interview: 'When most people make a mistake the consequences are not so severe as if I make a mistake – the patient could die. I am often required to make life and death decisions. This certainly makes my job stressful'.

3 *From your career*

(a) *Career mismatch*

You spend a high proportion of your working life at work. For this reason you need to be employed in a job which meets your needs and capabilities and provides you with the scope to fulfil your potential.

You may feel that you are in the wrong job, which itself creates stress. This can become apparent at particular stages in your life. Some people believe that life passes through a series of seven-year cycles. Frequently, when you complete a cycle you reappraise your situation and make changes if necessary. This can often happen between the ages of thirty-five and forty-five and is referred to as the 'mid-life' or 'mid-career crisis'.

Mark had just passed through the career decision-making phase when I interviewed him. He had been employed as a teacher in a comprehensive school.

'As a teacher I was beginning to feel quite disillusioned and stressed by the education system. The final straw came when I was asked to paint the classroom. Could you imagine a doctor being asked to paint the surgery, or a ward sister to paint the ward? I realized the time had come to find a job which more closely matched my needs and capabilities.'

He looked for a more suitable job in industry and was seeking a career in personnel.

(b) *Lack of clear goals*

You may feel you are in the right career, but no longer have clear goals or a sense of direction. This is another source of stress, particularly since career prospects have become more limited. You may experience stress when you realize your career path has begun to lack direction.

(c) *The 'plateaued' manager*

An extreme case of lack of goals and lack of opportunities is demonstrated by the 'plateaued' manager. Many organizations recruited staff in the late 1960s and 1970s, mapping out a career path for them. Now the impact of changing technology and the need for organizations to be competitive has reduced career opportunities.

Many managers are now finding that they are reaching their career ceiling much earlier than they had expected. Some of these managers have the capability to progress much further but the career openings are no longer available. For example, some of the banks have reorganized and bank staff are now experiencing this problem. Individuals obviously find this situation quite stressful.

4 *From relationships with colleagues, family and friends*

From relationships at work

Most managers spend nearly half their working lives interacting with others, consequently the importance of satisfactory relationships cannot be over-emphasized. Good working relationships enhance individual and organizational health. Poor working relationships are a major source of stress. As managers you need to develop effective working relationships at six levels:

- with your superiors
- with your colleagues
- with your subordinates
- with those who use your goods/services
- with those who supply you with goods/services
- with those whose decisions affect your status and resources.

At each level there is potential for stressful situations to develop.

(a) With superiors

A sound relationship based on trust and friendship enables you to react positively under pressure. Alternatively, several managers described relationships with their superiors as lacking in trust and support. If you find yourself in the latter situation you are far more likely to experience stress.

The relationship itself can also prove stressful. You may find you receive more criticism from a superior to whom you are less able to relate, and in moments of crisis you may feel you are handling the situation totally alone.

(b) With subordinates

To achieve your objectives as a manager you need to be able to relate to your subordinates. This may be a source of stress for you. The problem is linked to the problems of delegating tasks and meeting the needs of your subordinates. Some of you may feel it is easier to do the work yourself than spend valuable time getting work done by others.

(c) With colleagues

You may find relationships based on trust difficult to develop with colleagues. You may be in competition with them, and any weaknesses you reveal may weaken your position. A supportive relationship is therefore difficult to achieve, making the relationship more stressful.

In any relationship there is always the potential for a personality clash or conflict. If your experience has previously been more involved with things rather than people, for example engineering or accountancy, you are more likely to find relationships stressful.

(d) From relationships with your family and friends

These generate different forms of stress from those associated with work. Sometimes family and friends can have unrealistic expectations, or make heavy demands upon you – these may be reasonable or unreasonable. Stress may develop from these demands.

People have a basic need to relate to others. Relationships can become stressful if you feel misunderstood or rejected by others. The more intimate the relationship, the greater the feeling of vulnerability and potential for stress to develop.

5 *Outside work*

(a) From conflict between home and work

Reference was made in Step Two to the importance of an appropriate balance between home and work. Clearly, these two aspects of your life can often be in conflict and it is not always easy to find the right balance, as Richard explained.

Richard was a management consultant. His work took him away from home, often several nights a week. 'I just don't have enough time to do all I want to do. My family need me when I return home and I seem to have less and less time for myself.' He was divorced and took his family responsibilities seriously. At times he felt quite stressed, feeling a loyalty to his children's needs, but also an equally strong pull to pursue his career and be the breadwinner.

Unfortunately, just at the time when work demands are greatest, pressure on the home front can often be quite intense. Think back over your career. If you are in your late twenties or early thirties your career has probably reached an important stage. At this phase in your life you may also have a young family. This will be a greater or lesser strain depending on whether you are a man or a woman, and if you are a man whether your wife also works. Obviously, the strains of the dual-career family are much greater.

The number of dual-career families, where both partners pursue a career and at the same time raise a family, has increased over the years. The man has to play a more active role in the home. The woman has the task of fulfilling two roles and sometimes coping with emotions such as guilt.

6 Internal stressors

So far the stressors discussed have all been external factors. There are also a number of internal forces which create stress. These include:

(a) Your own expectations of yourself

You may set unrealistic goals and standards for yourself, strive to achieve them and become stressed in the process. This is partly related to personality. If you are the relaxed type you are less likely to operate this way than the ambitious type.

The process is, of course, self-perpetuating. Faced with a failure to achieve your targets, you lose self-confidence. There are lessons to be learnt from the book *In Search of Excellence* (see Further

Reading, page 158). It explains that part of the success of Rank Xerox salesmen is that they are set achievable sales targets. This builds up confidence and keeps sales on an upward spiral. Assess the standards you set yourself. Are they realistic or do you cause yourself unnecessary stress?

(b) A negative approach to life

There are a number of factors that result in a negative approach to life and can cause stress. The dominant emotion on these occasions is fear. This is a powerful feeling that seems to wipe out the capacity to think logically and robs the person of creativity. We have a number of fears, including:

i Fear of looking foolish.
If you are worried about appearing foolish you may avoid asking questions, or hold back and make a less valuable contribution. You need to be aware that people have this tendency, particularly when you are dealing with subordinates in a new job.

Fiona, a ward sister, related an amusing case taken from her early days in training. She was told by the staff nurse to give a patient a suppository. 'She asked if I knew how to give one.' As Fiona said 'I didn't want to look silly by saying I didn't know. I thought she had given me the clue when she told me to check the patient's breathing at the same time. I carefully inserted a suppository up each nostril, then noticed the paitent looked rather blue in the face. I asked the nurse to check that everything was correct. Of course the suppositories were in quite the wrong part of the patient. The nurse said she wouldn't have minded but I hadn't even taken their outer wrappings off!'

Fiona's case was amusing, but this is not always so in other cases. If you find yourself holding back you may find others take advantage of the situation. This can then become a source of stress for you when you realize you have difficulty putting across your point of view.

ii Fear of incompetence.
Several managers have referred to this as a source of stress. It could be associated with a time of rapidly changing technology and growing unemployment. Managers who have neared the ceiling of their careers may recognize this factor as a stressor. Suddenly

more junior managers start to overtake them and their fear of incompetence grows.

You may of course have fears of incompetence which are totally unfounded. If you set yourself very high standards you may decide the challenges are too great. Then fear becomes the dominant emotion. If this is a problem for you, later in the book you will learn to redirect the energy in a more positive way.

Your attitude to life is very important. You may also experience stress because of a tendency to expect the worst in every situation. This is obviously a far more stressful approach to life than that of those whose outlook is more optimistic.

(c) A negative self-image

You will also have a view of *yourself* – this picture is your self-image. Many of you probably have a positive view of yourself. Others may see themselves less favourably, or have no clear image. Being negative about yourself, or unclear of your image, creates internal tension and generates stress.

Your self-image develops, over a long period of time, from interaction with, and the comments of, people at work and at home. Very early on in life you decide whether you view yourself as superior, inferior or equal to the other people with whom you relate. This decision plays an important part in the image you build up of yourself. You make decisions about yourself in a number of ways:

- physical characteristics – attractive or unattractive
- intelligence
- sporting ability
- ability to relate to others
- ability to communicate
- capabilities in your job.

Reflect on your own self-image. Is it positive or negative? Do you have a clear picture of yourself? Do you need to take steps to develop it further?

(d) From internal demands and needs

Various people have theorized about needs. Needs provide the source of energy and help to explain your behaviour in different situations. Some needs are easily satisfied today, such as the need for food; others may be more elusive, such as the need to feel fulfilled. Whenever a need which is really important to you remains unsatisfied, it generates a feeling of frustration, or perhaps aggression, and can be a potential source of stress.

Edward was employed as a lecturer at a polytechnic. He had a high degree of commitment to work, playing an active role in the activities of his department. He was very ambitious and was striving for promotion. Some opportunities became available, but he was unsuccessful. Failure to satisfy his need caused him considerable stress.

Perhaps many of you can identify with Edward. At each level in the organizational hierarchy promotion becomes more restricted. Only a very small percentage of managers will become captains of industry. Others will have to come to terms with the situation. Those who fail to do so are far more likely to suffer from stress.

There is a range of needs which people seek to satisfy. These include:

- recognition
- social relationships
- status
- power
- achievement
- autonomy
- interesting work
- material rewards
- security.

Review your present situation and decide which needs are important to you. To what extent are these needs being met at present?

(e) From a lack of self-management

A common cause of stress, referred to earlier, is too much to do and not enough time to do it – the problem of overload. The root cause of stress may be a lack of self-management. Managers who cannot manage themselves, who waste time, fail to prioritize, and become inefficient will eventually become stressed. Could you be guilty of mismanaging yourself? Such people are often very busy, workaholics even, but at the end of the day have achieved little that relates to their objectives.

Failure to attend to your own wellbeing, discussed in Step Two, is another aspect of mismanaging yourself. Do you ensure you have adequate sleep and rest, and do you eat proper meals?

By now you should be clearer about the factors which cause stress. This is an important step in stress management. Another cause of stress is change. Step Five will help you assess the level of change in your life. You will then be in a much better position to develop a strategy to manage stress.

Step Five:
Assessing the level of change in your life

Stress is the outcome of a complex relationship between yourself and your environment. Throughout life you are faced with a whole series of changes, sometimes beyond your control, which have to be managed. The more changes you have to face, the more vulnerable you are to suffering from excessive stress. In Step Five you will assess the level of change in your life. Again, you need to repeat this step from time to time in order to keep a check on your stress level.

Life events which cause stress have been extensively researched. A ranking of stressful events was drawn up by researchers in the United States and is known as 'The Holmes and Rahe Social Readjustment Rating Scale'. The research was conducted across a range of cultures. A remarkable similarity was found in different cultural groups between the perceived importance of particular life events. The most stressful event, requiring the greatest adjustment, was considered to be the death of one's spouse, and was given a mean value of 100. Forty-two other events were rated in comparison with this event. The results are shown in the table 'Rating Scale of Life Events'.

Complete the exercise 'Assessing Life Events' to assess the level of change in your life.

Exercise: Assessing life events

Although the impact of life events is affected by your disposition (see Step One), it has proved helpful to review the impact of different forms of psychological pressure independently of the individual. This allows a level of objectivity to be gained.

Study the table of life events and mark off those you have experienced in the last year. Once you have marked them off go back and total up the values of each of the events you have experienced.

Rating scale of life events

Rank	Life event	Mean value
1	Death of spouse	100
2	Divorce	73
3	Marital separation	65
4	Jail term	63
5	Death of close family member	63
6	Personal injury or illness	53
7	Marriage	50
8	Fired at work	47
9	Marital reconciliation	45
10	Retirement	45
11	Change in health of family member	44
12	Pregnancy	40
13	Sexual difficulties	39
14	Gain of new family member	39
15	Business readjustment	39
16	Change in financial state	38
17	Death of close friend	37
18	Change to different line of work	36
19	Change in number of arguments with spouse	35
20	Mortage over £30,000	31
21	Foreclosure of a mortage or loan	30
22	Change in responsibilities at work	29
23	Son or daughter leaving home	29
24	Trouble with in-laws	29
25	Outstanding personal achievement	28
26	Wife begins or stops work	26
27	Begin or end school	26
28	Change in living conditions	25
29	Revision of personal habits	24
30	Trouble with boss	23
31	Change in work hours or conditions	20
32	Change in residence	20

Rank	Life event	Mean value
33	Change in school	20
34	Change in recreation	19
35	Change in church activities	19
36	Change in social activities	18
37	Mortgage or loan of £30,000 or less	17
38	Change in sleeping habits	16
39	Change in number of family get-togethers	15
40	Change in eating habits	15
41	Vacation	13
42	Christmas	12
43	Minor violations of the law	11

N.B. The figure for the mortgage has been adjusted from $10,000 to £30,000 to make it more realistic.

Interpreting your scores

A score of 100 or less. The amount of change you are currently facing is not too high at present. You should not be under excessive pressure from recent life-event changes.

A score of 101 to 200. The higher up this range you are the more likely you are to be experiencing the effects of pressure. You must have had a fairly high degree of change in the last year to have achieved a score of 250.

A score of 201 and over. You have obviously undergone some major changes in your life in the last year. You may need to pay particular attention, later in the book, to managing the effects of change.

This approach to diagnosing stress factors demonstrates a number of important points:

- Situations at home seem to be more stressful than those at work.
- Stress is the outcome of adding up all the life events you have experienced recently. You may, therefore, be very stressed because of several events in your life.
- Pleasant situations are stressful as well as unpleasant ones.
- The ranking scale is American. Work conducted in the UK

showed two differences. The mortgage in the UK ranked lower (managers have lower mortgages) and trouble with in-laws ranked higher (in-laws live closer).

The case of Martin and June demonstrates how one life event can trigger a series of events. Martin worked for a large computer company with a site in Scotland. They had two children who were at school, and June had just returned to work as a teacher, having had a spell at home bringing up the children. Suddenly, Martin was told he must relocate to the south east of England. This meant June had to give up her job, the children had to change schools, and they had to move away from their families and friends.

In their case they managed the change successfully. They received financial help from the firm for the move; each had emotional support from the other; and they moved to an area where they were quickly able to build up a circle of friends.

Review of step five

Before completing Step Five, review the changes you have faced in the last year with the help of the questions listed below:

1 Study the list on pages 63–4 and write down any of the items which you have experienced in the last year, along with its 'mean value'

2 Calculate your score and read the interpretation on page 64.

3 Note any additional life changes that are not listed and which have caused you stress in the last year.

4 How great was the impact of life changes on:

- Job performance.

- Relationships at home.

- Relationships at work.

- Physical wellbeing.

- Emotional wellbeing.

5 What were the most successful steps you took to adjust to the changes?

6 What were the least successful steps you took to adjust to the changes?

7 Consider each of the life events experienced and list those for which the adjustment process is still incomplete.

Step Six:
Spotting the warning signs

The purpose of this step is to spot the warning signs of excessive stress. Once you can do this before the effects start building up you have overcome a major obstacle to stress management. The quick identification of excessive stress is crucial for two reasons. Firstly, the detrimental effects are less likely to build up, consequently the impact on yourself and your employer is less severe. Secondly, people can recover much more quickly from a short period of excessive stress. Chronic stress necessitates a much longer recovery time, or leaves permanent damage. Think of the body like a piece of elastic stretched to its limit. Release the pull after a short time and the elastic returns to its original state. Maintain the pull longer and the elasticity is lost, making recovery impossible.

Several managers in the survey said they were unable to recognize the signs. They felt trapped on a treadmill, determined to keep the wheel in motion. The more they drove themselves to perform effectively, the more difficult the task became, until eventually they reached a state of total exhaustion. With hindsight they recognized the excessive pressure they had been under and its detrimental effect on work performance and the quality of their lives.

What are the signs that can warn you of excessive stress levels? Unfortunately, there is no straightforward answer. You may respond differently in very similar situations and your response pattern is likely to be unique. However, you may be able to identify certain typical responses which, in future, will alert you to the situation. These responses are mainly negative, but you may respond positively to stress. To help recognize your own symptoms of stress, complete the exercise 'Spotting the warning signs'.

Exercise: Spotting the warning signs

Read each of the statements listed below. If the statement applies, or has applied, to you in the previous twelve months, or at a time when you know you were experiencing intense pressure, then tick the statement. Be as honest as you can when you respond to the statement.

1____I am easily irritated.

2____I have difficulty concentrating for any length of time.

3____I feel tired even when I wake up in the morning.

4____I seem to have boundless energy.

5____I cannot take fairly trivial decisions.

6____The quality of my sleep has deteriorated. I have difficulty getting to sleep and/or I wake during the night and am very restless.

7____I am achieving far more work than usual.

8____I am losing my temper very frequently and feel powerful negative emotions.

9____I feel generally run-down and rather unwell.

10____I am able to concentrate fully on what I am doing.

11____Life seems to be quite hopeless. Nothing seems worthwhile and I feel really low.

12____My eating pattern has altered. I have lost my appetite, or I seem to be eating more food to comfort myself.

13____I have difficulty in absorbing new data.

14____I suffer from frequent headaches.

15____I am able to respond quickly to the demands placed upon me.

16——I have difficulty recalling information when I am required to do so.

17——I am drinking more alcohol than usual.

18——I experience dramatic swings of mood – sometimes I feel quite elated, at other times I feel really depressed.

19——I often feel exhilarated about what I am doing.

20——I have missed, or been late for, one or two important appointments.

21——I feel wound up and am unable to relax properly.

22——I am unable to achieve my normal level of creativity.

23——I suffer from backache regularly.

24——Ideas seem to flow more easily than usual.

25——I feel inadequate and unable to cope.

26——I have taken time off work.

27——I frequently suffer from indigestion.

28——I seem to lack the capacity to focus on a particular problem – my mind keeps wandering on to other issues.

29——The least little thing sends me into a panic. I feel as if I am unable to cope any more.

30——I have been smoking more cigarettes than usual.

31——I have a frequent need to urinate.

32——In discussion with other people I constantly repeat myself.

33——My driving is rather erratic and my judgement impaired.

34——I seem to have so many things to worry about.

35——I am mentally and/or physically very active.

Wherever you put a tick alongside a statement, put a 1 in the appropriate space below. Each number corresponds with the numbered statement on the preceeding pages. When you have done this, enter the totals of each of the columns in the spaces below.

Profile of warning signs

1___	2___	3___	6___	4___
8___	5___	9___	12___	7___
11___	13___	14___	17___	10___
18___	16___	21___	20___	15___
25___	22___	23___	26___	19___
29___	28___	27___	30___	24___
34___	32___	31___	33___	35___
Totals				
E___	T___	P___	B___	PR___

B—Emotional reactions
T—Disruption of thought processes
P—Physical illness
B—Behavioural indicators
PR—Positive reactions

Interpreting your scores

A score of 0–2. If you have scored zero in each category there are a number of possible interpretations. You may have been dishonest with yourself, or you may be unaware of the signs you are manifesting. You may, however, be managing your stress levels very effectively already.

A score of 2 in any category shows you have a tendency to react in a particular way to stressful situations.

A score of 3–5. If you have scored 3 or more in any one category this is likely to be a typical reaction. If you have scored in more than one category this may mean that you respond in different ways to different situations. Alternatively, you may have been suffering from excessive stress for a long time. This is now manifesting itself in several ways.

A score of 6–7. A score of 7 is common for some people from time to time, so do not add to your stress by worrying. Help is near at hand. Later steps will help you to manage your stress levels more effectively. First you need to understand the reactions a little more fully.

Interpreting your profile

The symptoms of stress which were most often mentioned by managers in the survey have been grouped into five categories for identification purposes:

1 E – Emotional reactions – feelings.
2 T – Disruption of thought processes – inability to think clearly.
3 P – Physical illness – ill-health.
4 B – Behavioural signs – changes in behaviour.
5 PR – Positive reactions – signs of thriving on pressure.

These categories are not mutually exclusive. For example, you may become very anxious (an emotional reaction) and also develop a headache (a physical sign). Sometimes you realize your behaviour has changed, for example you are unable to sleep. This change may be a result of illness or be related to emotional upheaval. Some years ago the reactions of people involved in speaking in public were studied. The researchers found that people who stuttered reported only moderate emotion, but they were clearly embarrassed (a behavioural reaction) and had an increased flow of adrenaline (a physical reaction).

Beware of immediately diagnosing excessive stress because you are suffering from a particular symptom. Once you read a book on stress a natural tendency is to assume you (and everyone else) are suffering from it. This may be true, but avoid jumping to conclusions too quickly. For example, if you suffer from a bad attack of indigestion there could be a physical reason for this which is unrelated to stress, or the food may be too rich!

During prolonged periods of stress you may react in different ways. At first you may react emotionally or be unable to think clearly. Ultimately you are likely to become emotionally and physically exhausted and, eventually, ill. Remember that the categories overlap and can lead from one to another. When you are learning to identify the warning signs you may find the process easier if you treat each category separately. A further explanation of each category follows, in order to help develop your understanding.

1 *Emotional reactions*

The way people respond emotionally to stress varies according to personality make-up, early upbringing and life experiences. Some people remain relaxed and easy-going, even when exposed to excessive pressure; others manage to build up even a trivial problem into a major disaster.

Reaction to excessive pressure intensifies personality characteristics. This means that as behaviour becomes more extreme, identification of emotional responses becomes easier. For example, the irritable person will explode at the least little thing, the inadequate person will collapse, and the anxious person will panic. Pause for a moment and think about your personality make-up. Which of your characteristics might become intensified in stressful situations?

When you were a child you probably experienced a wide range of feelings including:

anger   helplessness
depression   confusion
guilt   stupidity
frustration fear
boredom   inadequacy
hurt   triumph
timidity   jealousy

Gradually, you developed particular feelings which you continue to re-experience in adult life. Parents influence the choice, discouraging anger for example, but condoning helplessness. Consequently our emotional reactions are not always appropriate to a particular situation.

Bruce had been discouraged as a child from displaying anger and aggression. He had been brought up with three younger sisters and had been taught to stifle feelings of aggression and anger. The particular feeling he developed was confusion, a feeling he repeatedly re-lived in later life. Under stressful circumstances this feeling dominated. If, for example, he was in conflict with colleagues, instead of an angry outburst, which could be viewed as appropriate behaviour, he would become confused, a somewhat inappropriate reaction to the situation. Colleagues would often misinterpret this behaviour, making the situation even more stressful for Bruce.

Identifying your typical emotional reactions will need an awareness of how you feel in particular situations, for example, feeling low or elated. Look back at the list and try to identify your typical feelings. Alternatively, you may find you are more able to recognize a behavioural sign, for example, a sudden outburst of temper.

Important emotional reactions that are stress related include:

- irritability
- anger and aggression
- anxiety
- a feeling of hopelessness – depression
- swings of mood from elation to despondency
- withdrawal from people.

Irritability

Most people will occasionally feel irritable. This is a natural reaction to the annoyances of life which we perpetually encounter. This reaction provides us with a useful barometer for measuring and recognizing excessive stress levels.

- Does the least little thing annoy you?
- Has your life become a battlefield moving from one argument to another?
- Are you always expressing dissatisfaction with people or situations?
- Do you find every other driver on the road a source of irritation?

If you answer yes to these questions, could you be suffering from excessive stress? Certainly some of the people I interviewed experienced irritability when they were suffering from stress.

Mary worked as a teacher, combining her career with bringing up a family. The job suited her circumstances well: her children were at school during term-time and Mary was able to be at home during school holidays. However, during term-time Mary felt particularly overloaded. As term progressed she realized she had become more and more irritable, particularly with her own family.

At home she was always shouting at the children and complaining about their behaviour. She felt unable to relax and enjoy life. Many working mothers will probably identify with Mary.

Anxiety

Anxiety tends to be a common reaction to stressful events and is probably the most important one. For many, anxiety is never far below the surface, particularly during times of change, giving rise to a fear of the unknown and leading the person to anticipate catastrophe. Even the most trivial events will be viewed as a source of stress.

A certain level of anxiety is quite normal. We all become anxious before, for example, a visit to the dentist, or a particularly important meeting or job interview. The over-anxious person will exaggerate every event out of all proportion.

James was always an anxious person, but when he heard that he had been promoted to supermarket manager his anxiety level rose dramatically. He used to wake up in a sweat, terrified he might oversleep and be late opening the store for his staff. Would they all turn up on time for work and what would he do if the deliveries were late? By the time he reached work he was a nervous wreck, and so his day continued. James was constantly thinking of the next possible disaster and became irritable and tired. Eventually his area manager suggested he reappraise his life. Only then did James realize the extent of his anxiety and the detrimental effect it was having on his work performance.

Depression

If you experience prolonged feelings of pessimism, despair and despondency, you could be suffering frrom depression. If you have had the occasional feeling of unhappiness when things have gone wrong, don't conclude that you were suffering from depression. This is a matter of degree – you inevitably have the occasional bout of 'the blues', but when this reaction occurs regularly you may be depressed. A common feeling associated with depression is inadequacy, resulting in loss of self-esteem.

Dennis described his job as a financial services manager in a company undergoing excessive change. He talked in a dull, monotonous voice, complaining of his inability to cope with the demands being made upon him. 'Everyone else seems able to stay on top of the situation; I just seem unable to manage the change. On top of everything at work, I have been rather low at home, and now my wife is threatening divorce. There seems to be no future ahead of me.'

Dennis is possibly fairly typical of the depressed person. Awareness of the problem is half the battle. You can then take steps to alleviate pressure and become less emotional.

If you react emotionally to stress, which emotions are you most likely to experience? Once you have identified them you will greatly improve your ability to manage stress.

2 *Disruption of thought processes*

Another warning sign of excessive stress which is experienced by managers is the inability to think clearly, or the 'disruption of thought processes'. Specific examples ranged from a loss of concentration to indecision and loss of memory. These particular manifestations of stress have important implications for your overall effectiveness. The problem of your inability to think clearly leads to a decrease in performance. This causes more stress and traps you in a vicious circle.

Four thought processes are likely to be disrupted by stress:

- receiving information
- problem-solving and decision-making
- creativity
- retrieval of information.

Receiving information

Throughout life you are constantly bombarded with a whole range of data, including facts, ideas, attitudes and beliefs. You mainly receive this data through your senses of sight and hearing. Some are within your range of awareness; other data are beyond it and therefore never received.

At any one moment you only absorb a proportion of the information available. The amount you absorb depends on your attentiveness. This is influenced by motivation to listen and your level of understanding of the information. If the information is unfamiliar, you can easily become overloaded and unable to absorb any of it. Stress also affects your receptiveness to data.

At an optimum stress level you are far more able to concentrate and be receptive to new data. Once you become over-stressed your ability to concentrate drops and you are less aware of the outside world. In this situation you might sometimes describe yourself as forgetful. The problem is more likely to be a lack of attention.

Mark was a higher executive officer in the Civil Service. He was required to attend a range of meetings and produce the minutes. He was a conscientious individual and his superiors were always confident of his ability to report meetings accurately. Suddenly he started to make mistakes and miss out important information. No one could understand what had happened to Mark. In fact, he had been going through a divorce and was under severe stress as a result. The effect was a loss of concentration at work.

Alvin Toffler (see Further Reading, page 158) referred to the impact of the changing environment on people, where the requirement is to adapt continually and rapidly to unpredictable situations. Quite quickly you become over-stimulated, bombarded with too much new data. You are likely to become confused, disorientated, or to distort reality. The new data is therefore received inaccurately.

Problem-solving and decision-making

As a manager you need to be an effective problem-solver. To achieve this you need to be able to think rationally and logically and focus your mind on the problem. When you are over-stressed all these processes become more difficult. You may have heard people say 'I have so much on my mind I just cannot think straight.' Faced with over-stress, a common reaction is to flit from one thing to another and achieve very little. You may experience difficulty in focusing your mind on one specific problem.

You also need clarity of thought to be able to think through problems rationally and logically and make effective decisions. When you become over-stressed all these processes become more difficult. This is partly because the inability to think as a result of excessive pressure is often accompanied by a headache. A manager may report feeling as if his head is about to burst.

Faced with problems and the need to take decisions, the over-stressed manager is more likely to become incompetent. Effective problem-solving requires a systematic approach, a clear view of objectives, analysis of alternatives and a decision on a course of action. John Adair in *Effective Decision-Making* (see Further Reading, page 158) comments that stress impairs thinking, affects the quality of decisions and causes people to vacillate. Effective decision-making requires time spent in concentrated thought. The over-stressed person always feels that time is a scarce commodity.

- Do you experience difficulty in thinking clearly?
- Do you sometimes make the wrong decisions?
- Do you sometimes vacillate?
- Do you avoid making decisions?

If you answer 'yes' to these questions stress could be affecting the quality of your decision-making.

Creativity

Excessive stress also seems to stifle creativity. To be creative and generate new ideas you need to focus your mind and let the ideas flow. If you are over-stressed you probably have difficulty concentrating and getting in touch with the ideas. Sometimes the creative process can occur but you are unable to retrieve the ideas from your brain. Only when you relax do the ideas flow. As one manager said, 'I can spend hours at work trying to come up with a creative solution without success. I go home, have a meal, perhaps watch some TV, then, relaxing in a bath, the solution suddenly comes to me.'

Christine worked as a marketing executive. She had ten staff reporting to her and her boss made heavy demands on her time. She felt continually under too much pressure and found her level of creativity impaired. Eventually, with careful time management, she arranged two clear days at the end of each month and always worked at home on these days to avoid interruption. She found making this time available enhanced her creative ability.

Retrieval of information

Have you ever been about to introduce someone and suddenly their name escapes you? This often happens when the circumstances are stressful and you have reacted by freezing. This prevents you from being able to recall the person's name. If you know the people well you may react by saying, 'I'm sorry, your name is on the tip of my tongue.' More often you are left feeling extremely embarrassed, which of course further increases your stress level.

3 *Physical illness*

Medical experts generally agree that many illnesses are stress-related. Research has shown that chronic stress lowers resistance to illness and intensifies its impact. Even if your score for physical illness was zero do not skip this section. You need to be aware of the illnesses thought to be stress-related. The following list summarizes those illnesses most frequently mentioned by experts.

Take a moment to reflect on your own health record. Have you experienced periods of ill-health? If you have been ill:

- Did the illness coincide with stressful periods of your life?
- Have you had recurring ailments and health problems over the years?
- Have you suffered different patterns of illness over your life span?

Some stress-related illnesses, such as coronary diseases, are killers. Other physical effects are less severe. You may experience non-specific pain or just feel generally unwell. The impact of stress depends on the severity and duration of the pressure and your own vulnerability to it. Most people have one or two weak spots in their bodies. Prolonged stress can often lead to a particular physical response, depending on your point of weakness.

Most of the managers interviewed experienced a certain amount of stress-related illness. Sarah, an accountant with a firm in the City, once experienced a chronic attack of sinusitis which lasted several months. This coincided with her final examinations for Chartered Accountancy. The sinuses became her weak spot. Subsequently she reported inflamation of the sinuses accompanied

Stress-related illnesses

Mouth
Ulcers

Cardiovascular system
Heart attack
Palpitations
Hypertension (high blood pressure)
Angina
Migraine
Haemorrhoids

Digestive tract
Colic
Diarrhoea/constipation
Indigestion and heartburn
Ulcers
Diabetes

Reproductive organs
Premenstrual tension (f)
Impotence (m)
Menstrual disorders (f)

Lungs
Asthma
Coughs
Dizziness
Fainting
Breathlessness/Breathing difficulties

Hair
Alopecia

Skeletal-Muscular system
Muscular twitches
Back-ache
Neck-ache
Tension headache
Arthritis
Gnashing of teeth

Bladder
Irritability and need to urinate frequently

Skin
Eczema
Psoriasis

by severe headaches. She realized that these attacks always coincided with stressful periods in her life, for example at the end of the financial year.

You may respond very differently. David, working in the publishing industry, was perpetually required to meet deadlines. He had recently married and was under considerable pressure at work. He seemed to survive during the week, but every weekend, when he relaxed, he complained of indigestion and other pains. Friends joked about his wife's cooking. Eventually he consulted a doctor and an ulcer was diagnosed. Shortly afterwards he changed his job and his health problems cleared up. He has, incidentally, remained happily married!

This last example demonstrates how symptoms of stress are not always apparent at the time of acute pressure. Only when you relax do the symptoms appear. Many people experience health problems at weekends or on holiday, or shortly after a period of excessive pressure. Sometimes health problems resulting from stress occur as much as a year after the stressful event.

Occasionally, treatment of physical illness can have a detrimental effect on work performance. You may no longer be sensitive to your own stress levels. A consultant once gave an example of this. He was visited by a business executive suffering from haemorrhoids (known to be stress-related). The consultant agreed to operate and saw the executive two months after the operation for a check-up. Asked whether the operation had been successful, the executive's response was unenthusiastic. He explained that he negotiated contracts for his company. Before the operation, he experienced a sharp pain from the haemorrhoids as tension built up. This was his sign that it was time to close the negotiations. Without the haemorrhoids he no longer knew the exact moment to close.

4 *Behavioural signs*

This category includes changes in behaviour that can be observed and recognized more easily, particularly by other people. If you are over-stressed your behaviour may suggest a desire to escappe, for example by avoiding contact with people. Your behaviour

may reveal an attempt to console yourself, for example through excessive eating or drinking.
The range of behaviour includes:

● Poor sleeping habits
● Excessive drinking
● Excessive eating/loss of appetite
● Missed appointments/lateness
● Avoiding contact with people/time off work
● Changed driving behaviour

Poor sleeping habits

Insomnia is a common sign of stress. You may be unable to relax and forget your problems, have difficulty getting to sleep, and your sleep disturbed by dreams or waking in the night.

Robin normally slept well until his new boss joined the organization. He gradually realized that as soon as he got into bed he started thinking about work. Robin was a systems analyst working for a local authority. In the past he had been given the freedom to run his own projects, but his new boss kept interfering. Robin became tired, irritable and tense. Finally he decided he would confront his boss. He managed to persuade him to delegate more and give him more freedom to manage his own work. Robin also resolved to relax more in the evenings, realizing that his boss might not change. Gradually the sleepless nights lessened and Robin felt much less tense.

Pause for a moment and reflect on the quality of your sleep.

● Do you ever experience problems getting to sleep?
● Do you wake in the night?
● Is your sleep disturbed?
● Do you have vivid dreams?

The stressed person often suffers insomnia.

Excessive drinking

Alcoholism is a growing problem facing organizations today. TThis may be a sign of increased stress. People who resort to drink are seeking refuge from their problems. Drink does nothing to solve the problem, it just makes it easier to bear.

Malcolm was a consultant with an advertising agency. He was required to entertain clients regularly, and he drank with them. His agency lost one or two valuable accounts and colleagues blamed Malcolm. He found himself drinking more and more until in the end he could not face making a presentation to a client without having a drink first. Colleagues warned him of his excessive drinking, but he seemed unable to stop himself. He became more and more incoherent, he lost his creativity and flair and, ultimately, the problem cost Malcolm his job.

Sadly, Malcolm's case is a common one today. Alcohol dulls the brain, impairs work performance and damages the reputation of the organization. Often, people suffering from alcoholism find difficulty in recognizing and overcoming the problem.

- Do you find yourself drinking at lunchtime more often?
- Do you need a drink rather than enjoy one?
- Do you immediately pour a drink on your return home?
- Do you drink alone?

If you answer yes to these questions you may be suffering from stress.

Avoiding contact with people/time off work

People who prefer solitude and time on their own – sometimes described as introverts – are more likely to react to stress by avoiding people or staying off work. Over-stressed people usually feel fatigued, and introverts find the wear and tear of social contact too much to manage. Most jobs, especially in management, require a high level of contact with people, which may over-tax the stressed person.

Driving behaviour

Driving is a skill which requires vigilant behaviour, judgement and tolerance of other road-users. Many people, on becoming enclosed in their cars, take on new personalities – the quiet person can become quite aggressive, etc.

Sally, a sales representative, said her first warning of stress was a change in her style of driving. In particular, if a customer upset her she became preoccupied and more accident-prone; her judgement of distances seemed to go. She also found difficulty in parking the car.

5 Positive reactions to stress

So far the signs of stress have been negative, but the effects can be positive. Focus on a time when you have been working under fairly intense pressure and performing well. How were you feeling at the time?

Several managers in the survey described times when they responded to pressure in a positive way. Some of you will need and enjoy a fairly high level of pressure in your lives. The managers interviewed talked of flowing with the pressure, feeling full of energy and enthusiasm and able to accomplish much greater volumes of work than usual.

What they were describing was the effect of the physiological stress reaction. Their bodies were full of adrenaline which was making them much more alert and active. Apparently, actors need to feel a certain level of stress to perform well. A study was made of actors who forgot their lines. This nearly always happened when they felt too relaxed.

Responding to stress in a positive way enables you, therefore, to flow with the pressure, but, as with negative reactions, it should not be allowed to continue for long periods of time. You are just as likely to end up burnt out if you don't pace yourself correctly.

Implications of stress reactions

You are now aware of the range of possible reactions to stress. These reactions are far-ranging and could have devastating consequences for yourself, your employer and for your home life.

Yourself

A fair description of an overstressed person might be unhappy, ill-tempered and ill at ease. Certainly, life ceases to be fun, work performance deteriorates and relationships with colleagues and people outside work suffer. After prolonged stress you are most likely to be experiencing ill-health.

Your employer

Your employer cannot afford to operate with his workforce over-stressed. The outcome will be decreased work performance and productivity, a higher level of absenteeism, poor decision-making and the inability of employees to manage time effectively.

Home life

Regrettably, the consequences of stress at work are likely to affect home life. How many wives complain that their executive husbands have changed – forever preoccupied with work and withdrawn from the family? Alternatively, people who react emotionally to stress are often more able to control their emotions at work, waiting until they get home to let off steam.

Review

You are now aware that stress manifests itself in a range of ways. The early warning signs may be physical or emotional, and may be perceived as positive or negative. Ultimately, the effects are likely to result in ill-health if allowed to continue unchecked.

Recognizing that you are suffering from excessive stress is one of the most important steps in managing stress. For this reason, spend a little more time reflecting on the way you respond to stress. You may also like to collect the views of friends and colleagues to enable you to spot the warning signs and manage the situation quickly.

List below the five most important signs that tell you that you are suffering from stress:

1. ....

2. ....

3. ....

4. ....

5. ....

Part 2
Review and consolidation

Step Seven:
Weighing up the balance and developing a vision of the future

Having completed the diagnosis you should have a fairly good idea of the factors contributing to stress. Before moving to the final section, designed to help you develop your techniques and strategies for managing stress, it is helpful to review and consolidate.

Managing stress successfully comes from clear answers to the following questions

1 Where am I now, i.e. what is my current stress level?
2 Where do I want to be, i.e. what stress level do I want to maintain in my life?
3 How do I get there, i.e. what are the appropriate techniques to help me achieve the right balance?

Where am I now?

To bring Steps One to Six together and assess your current stress level you need to 'weigh up the balance'. This involves answering the question:
Do demands on you outweigh your capacity, or are your resources inadequate to meet demands?

Exercise: weighing up the balance

Because stress occurs when you perceive an imbalance between demands and your capacity to meet those demands, you need to weigh up these two sets of factors. Once you have done this you will be in a better position to select an appropriate strategy to manage stress.

Review the diagnostic steps – including Steps One, Two, Four and Five – and answer the following questions:

1 Does your disposition make you more or less resistant to stress? (See Step One.)

2 How vulnerable are you to stress in terms of lifestyle? (See Step Two.)

3 What are the major demands facing you currently? (See Step Four.)

4 How much change have you needed to manage in the last twelve months? (See Step Five.)

5 Would you describe your current stance on life as basically positive or negative?

6 How would you describe your stress level? Too high; about right; too low?

Weighing up the balance

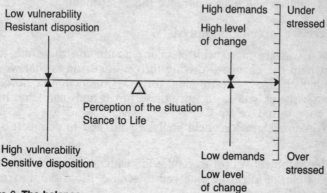

Figure 6 **The balance**

Figure 6 shows that:

1 A balanced state occurs when disposition and vulnerability are equally matched by demands and level of change. In this situation you are unlikely to suffer from stress.
2 An imbalanced state occurs, causing you to become over-stressed, when demands and level of change are high and you are highly vulnerable and have a sensitive disposition.
3 An imbalanced state occurs, causing you to become under-stressed, when your vulnerability is low, you have a resistant disposition and demands and level of change are low.

To complete this exercise answer the following three questions:
1 Am I experiencing excessive stress?

2 If I am experiencing excessive stress what are the reasons?

3 Am I experiencing insufficient stress at times? Do I need to raise my stress level to enhance work performance?

To select an appropriate strategy to manage stress you need to assess the options available. Completing what is called a force-field analysis will help you make this assessment.

Exercise: force-field analysis

When you are faced with changing a situation there are forces that help the change – driving forces – and forces that work to inhibit change – restraining forces. Conducting a forcefield analysis helps you to identify these forces and plan what has to be done to reduce stress.

To complete a forcefield analysis you need to complete seven steps:

1 Set an objective, for example: life without excessive stress.
2 List all the forces helping you to achieve life without excessive stress (the driving forces).
3 List all the forces stopping you from achieving life without stress (the restraining forces).
4 Identify people who control any of the forces.
5 Estimate the relative strength of each force. You could show this by drawing arrows, the longer the arrow the greater the strength.
6 Analyse each force and decide what you could do to increase smaller driving forces and decrease larger restraining forces.
7 Make a list of actions in order of priority.

Complete the exercise by filling out the table opposite. Draw in the arrows on each side of the centre line. Short lines indicate weak forces, longer lines indicate stronger forces. Write the force alongside each arrow. When you have completed the table make a list of action, in order of priority, of the steps you must take to increase driving forces and decrease restraining forces.

Force-field Analysis

Objective. . . . .

Driving forces	Restraining forces
....	....
....	....
....	....
....	....
....	....
....	....
....	....
....	....

My list of action in order of priority is:

Where do you want to be?

An alternative way of deciding what has to be done is to develop a vision of the future. Jerry, a production manager at a light engineering company who had just come through a very stressful period in his life, said, 'I thought I would never feel the same again after a series of catastrophes. One day I was out walking and thought: Why don't I try managing my life in the same way I manage my job? I went home and asked myself the question: What do I want from life? At the time I was feeling highly stressed, so I felt I wanted to be without stress. I wrote down a list of things which I would associate with a stress-free life. It looked something like this . . .' He jotted down a list of things, including some of those listed below.

- Feeling full of energy.
- Able to sleep well at night and wake up refreshed.
- A sharp mind able to concentrate well.
- Enjoying a satisfying emotional relationship.
- Able to like and enjoy people.
- A successful career.
- Optimistic about life and the future.
- Taking plenty out of life and putting plenty back in.

To effect change in your life you need to have a vision of where you want to go. In the same way as you might manage a situation at work, you need objectives and a plan of how you are going to achieve them. You will also need criteria for success. All of these are achievable once you have a vision.

Exercise: a vision of the future

A vision of the future is defined as a clear, visual, integrated picture, in sufficient focus to provide the basis for action planning. To develop this vision you will need to choose a quiet time when you have a couple of hours uninterrupted. When you find the time, complete the following steps:

1 Think back over at least the last ten years and write out a description of your life, with particular reference to stress. Include in this:

- Key life events related to work and outside work.
- Your thoughts and feelings at the time.
- Your state of health and energy level.
- Any stress and the symptoms.
- How you attempted to cope with the stress.

2 Read your description and ask yourself:

- Are there any recurring themes?
- What causes me stress and what are the signs?
- Is there anything I want to change?
- What would I like to be different?
- Do I want to increase or reduce my stress level?

3 Write a short description of your future life, again with particular reference to stress. Include in your description all those items you would like to change or be different. Include your preferred stress level.

Once you have completed Step Seven you should have a clearer view of where you are and where you want to be. Section Three will help you to achieve your objectives by providing you with strategies for managing stress.

Part 3
Strategies and techniques for managing stress

Introduction

You are now ready to embark on the next section of the book. On its completion you should have evolved your own techniques and strategies for managing stress. These will link closely with the vision of the future that you identified in the previous step. You will need to reflect on previous attempts at managing stress and will need a high degree of commitment to experiment with new ways of managing stress.

First, you need to adopt a positive approach to stress. A certain amount of stress is inevitable and beneficial, particularly if you work in a situation which is constantly changing. Your reaction to stress provides you with the extra energy needed to respond to change. Without that extra energy you would find the change process far more difficult.

You may still view stress negatively. If you are the Conscientious Type, you may have a fear of stress and go to great lengths to avoid it. By looking at stress in this way you are allowing fear to stunt your growth. The Anxious Type also mishandles stress by directing pressure inwards and becoming self-destructive.

Second, people vary in their capacity to manage stress. Some people seem able to withstand periods of stress as their lives undergo rapid change. These may be followed by phases of less hectic activity to allow time for recovery. People who structure their lives in this way are more able to manage stress. Others, such as the Ambitious and Lively Types, lead highly pressurized lives, moving from one demanding situation to another and never allowing time for relaxation. They may not realize the ultimate price they may have to pay – that of burn-out. Far better to learn how to manage stress.

Lessons on how to manage stress can be learnt by studying the way sportsmen and women and musicians handle stress. They have to operate at peak performance and need to maintain the balance. Those who are highly successful have learnt to enhance their performance by operating in full control of the situation. The level of pressure is neither too great nor too low.

Once you experience stress there are a number of management strategies you can adopt in order to cope with the situation. Some of these strategies are successful, depending on your personality characteristics and the situation in which you find yourself. Others are less successful and failure to manage the situation will further increase your stress level. You need to be able to identify less effective coping mechanisms so that you can avoid these in future.

There are several broad strategies for managing stress. You can actually prevent stress from occurring in the first place. This is advisable if the effects of stress are likely to be associated with insufficient or excessive pressure, and will help you to optimize stress. The second step will help you to recognize ineffective coping mechanisms. The third step will help you adopt successful strategies for the management of stress. Once you have completed this section you will feel much more able to handle the challenges which lie ahead of you.

Step Eight:
Optimizing stress levels

Successful stress management requires you to optimize the situation in which you find yourself. This means getting the best possible results in a given set of circumstances. To help achieve this you need to be able to maintain the balance between capabilities and demands.

Some of you may feel that in today's society you are required to work or live in situations that are unbalanced. In other words, you may find demands placed upon you, either by others or self-imposed, which are either too great or not demanding enough for your capabilities and resources. This is inevitable, and life would be rather dull without challenges to be met and without the need to develop strengths.

Step Eight has two main aims:

1 To help you understand the balance between demands and capabilities, and their relationship to work performance.
2 To help you work in ways which will maximize performance: by rising to challenges, building self-confidence, developing commitment and maintaining a degree of control over your situation.

The relationship between pressure, stress and performance

Everyone needs a certain level of pressure in order to perform. It provides the stimulation necessary for creativity and innovation. Without pressure your output and development are likely to be limited.

Some stress is also beneficial. When you feel you have insufficient resources to meet a situation the stress reaction is triggered and creates the extra energy needed for extremely demanding situations. It can be viewed as the 'spice of life' which will help you be innovative, explore unknown territory, and will supply you with the zest for living. This type of stress enhances performance when you flow with the pressure.

Stress can also be destructive. If this is the case you will notice a dramatic fall-off in your performance. When stress becomes negative it saps your energy and distorts your perspective on life. Negative stress can arise from too much or too little pressure, as Figure 7 illustrates.

This figure is best explained by comparing the performances of three sales managers giving sales presentations. Nicholas was required to make a sales presentation to a group of executives from companies that could be potential clients. He was keen to make a good impression and before he started the presentation he felt the flow of adrenaline that accompanies the stress reaction. This gave the energy he needed to perform at his peak. He always prepared well beforehand, so throughout the presentation he felt in control. When executives asked him questions at the end he again felt stimulated by the pressure and was able to perform at his best.

In this first case Nicholas was operating between **B** and **C**. Pressure was enhancing his performance, not inhibiting it by being insufficient or excessive. Performance improves as the stress level rises, up to a certain point.

By contrast, George was required to make a similar presentation to a group of sales representatives he knew well. It came at a busy time for him, just when he had made the presentation at least six times already that week. He went into feeling tired and bored. He felt none of the adrenaline experienced by Nicholas and the presentation he made was rather low key. Questions at the end of the sessions were limited and several of the reps themselves looked rather bored.

George had been operating in the **A** to **B** part of the curve. He experienced very little stimulation from the situation and consequently his performance was rather mediocre. When operating in the **A** to **B** part of the curve feelings of apathy, frustration and boredom are likely.

Figure 7: **Relationship between pressure, stress and performance**

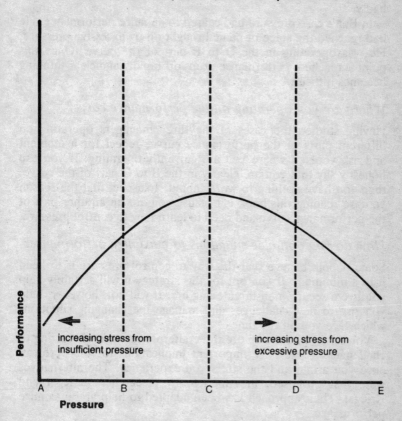

Ben, the third sales manager, was required to give a sales presentation at which his boss was present. The relationship between himself and his boss was poor and Ben always felt rather anxious when his boss was present. He thought he had done the necessary preparation, but, unfortunately, during the presentation several technical problems arose, including the breakdown of the film projector. The film made an important contribution to the presentation. Ben felt his level of stress rise considerably, his

planning was forgotten and the last part of the presentation went
badly.

In Ben's case pressure had ceased to enhance performance. He
had reached the stage of panic brought on by excessive pressure.
He was operating in the **D** to **E** part of the curve. Once this
point is reached, performance drops off rapidly and clear thinking
becomes difficult.

Where are you operating on the performance curve?

Having studied the cases of the three managers operating on
different parts of the performance curve, reflect for a moment
and ask yourself where you are currently operating. If you can
honestly say that you are clearly in the **B** to **C** part of the curve,
then you have nothing to worry about. I suspect that the reason
you are reading this book is because you are on another part of
the performance curve and need to learn how to control pressure.

How do you optimize situations to maximize performance?

Some people believe that the way to control pressure is to keep
it to a minimum. If you opt for this strategy it will certainly help
you live a secure, non-threatening life. It will not, however, help
you rise to new challenges and manage the changing situations
which face you all the time.

You might like to explore three alternative ways of reacting to
challenges. These have important implications for the performance you attain and the stress you experience. The alternatives
were first proposed, in America, by researchers Kriegal and
Kriegal. Their approach has been adapted to help you maximize
performance.

The way you react to situations depends on two factors:

1 Your perception of your competence level.
2 Your perception of the level of challenge in the situation.

The relationship is best understood with the aid of a diagram.

There are three ways of reacting to situations, depending on
the level of challenge and your competence in the situation.

1 Flight reaction – when the challenge is low, but your competence
is high.

Figure 8: **Relationship between performance, demands and capability**

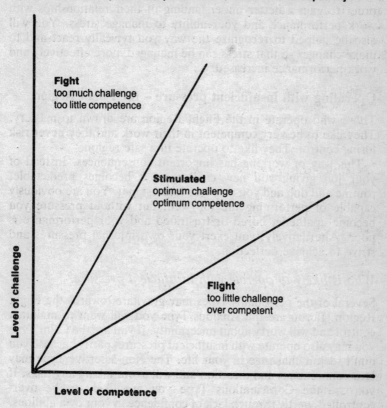

Fight
too much challenge
too little competence

Stimulated
optimum challenge
optimum competence

Flight
too little challenge
over competent

Level of challenge

Level of competence

2 Fight reaction – when there is too much challenge, but you lack competence.
3 Stimulated reaction – when there is optimum challenge and optimum competence.

Your reactions are also related to:

● Your level of self-confidence.
● Your degree of commitment.
● Your degree of control over the situation.

We will discuss the three reactions, as they relate to challenge, in order to gain a better understanding of their relationships with work performance and your ability to manage stress. You will also be helped to recognize the way you typically react and to make changes so that stress can be managed more effectively and work performance increased.

Operating with insufficient pressure – the Flight Region

Those who operate in the Flight Region are drawn to mastery. They like to be very competent in their work and they never risk losing control. They like to operate in a safe region.

This way of working has important consequences. Instead of your job giving you new challenges, it becomes predictable, routine and dull and you may lose interest in it. You are obviously capable of performing the job well, but without pressure you become apathetic, bored or frustrated and your performance is poor. Alternatively, you exert your own internal pressures and strive to achieve perfection.

Who is likely to operate with insufficient pressure?

Several of the personality types may gravitate towards the Flight Region. If you are the Anxious Type you will want to maintain control and will worry about uncertainty. If you are the Calm Type you may also operate with insufficient pressure, partly because you don't seek a challenge in your life. The Non-assertive Type may lack commitment and direction and will avoid taking any risks. If you are the Conscientious Type you are likely to be over-controlled, partly through lack of confidence in your own abilities.

The stress of operating with insufficient pressure

If you find yourself in a situation which lacks challenge, but you are tied to the job for security reasons the situation is likely to become stressful. You may feel frustrated, resentful or depressed. The energy from stress is directed inwards and can be highly destructive and result in depressive illnesses.

What to do if you operate in the Flight Region

You must learn to take a few risks, stretch yourself, make a few mistakes and start to rise to challenges. Get the adrenaline flowing and don't keep too tight a control on yourself; allow yourself a little more freedom to experiment.

One barrier to success is telling yourself you cannot do things. You lack confidence in yourself, and even when you do take a few risks you may not be fully committed to what you are doing. You don't *believe* you will succeed, and this becomes a self-fulfilling prophecy, so you fail. Adopt a more positive approach to situations and you are far more likely to succeed. You will learn how to do this by learning how to operate in the Stimulated Region.

You may find yourself lacking challenge because you have been doing the same job for too long. In this case consider a job move, or look for ways of doing different tasks or working differently in order to raise your level of adrenaline.

Operating with excessive pressure – the Fight Region

If you operate in the Fight Region you are drawn to challenging situations. You are likely to be very highly motivated to succeed and to have a need for achievement, or a liking for risks. You become over-committed, over-challenged and out of control. You are likely to want to do too much in too little time.

Is this an effective way to operate? No, because you drive yourself too hard and never have time to stand back and review your situation. Creativity is likely to be hampered by operating in a frenzy. You need time for creative ideas to flow. You may achieve less than someone who is not so over-committed.

Who is likely to operate with excessive pressure?

The ambitious manager and the carefree ('lively') manager are the types most likely to operate in the Fight Region. If you are an Ambitious Type you are likely to be driven by the need for achievement and thus become over-committed.

If you are the Lively Type you are likely to be driven by the need for risk-taking and challenge. You may put yourself into situations that are beyond your capabilities.

Some of you may find yourselves operating in the Fight Region when you normally operate in the Flight Region. Often, those of you who fear uncertainty may, in an attempt to get out of your rut, find yourselves operating with too much haste. Before you know where you are, you find yourself in a panic situation and totally out of control. This reinforces your need for security and you return to a more secure way of working – back in the Flight Region.

The stress of working with excessive pressure

If you are in a situation where you are reacting to events, you are likely to use up quite a lot of nervous energy without actually achieving a great deal – a lot of energy is wasted in useless effort. Operating in this way is likely to drive you beyond your reserves of energy. In the Fight Region you are most likely to experience exhaustion, burn-out or heart attacks.

What to do if you operate in the Fight Region

If you are operating in the Fight Region you may be driven by the idea 'I have to turn up and achieve.' There is always a race against time; a keenness to complete the task. You need to learn to keep control of your eagerness. Learn towards stand back; take time to plan and prepare; channel your energy towards achieving goals, rather than operating in an uncontrolled way. You will also see how to achieve this by learning how to operate in the Stimulated Region.

What does it feel like to operate in the Stimulated Region?

Most of you, at some time or another, will have experienced what it is like to operate at peak performance under pressure. Reflect for a moment and think of an occasion when you achieved peak performance. Perhaps you can think of an occasion at work, or while playing your favourite sport or playing a musical instrument?

● What was your specific experience?

● What were your feelings at the time?

- How would you describe yourself at the time?

Those who have described the experience of operating in the Stimulated Region regularly include a number of qualities:

- Transcendence – you achieve beyond your normal limits and are more effective than usual.
- Effortlessness – your performance comes easily, without having to try hard.
- Positiveness – you are confident that you will achieve, rather than just *trying* to achieve. You feel good about what you are doing.
- Spontaneity – your responses seem to flow naturally. You feel in good humour and your choices come easily.
- Being focused – your mind is completely on what you are doing. You have absolute concentration.
- Vitality – you feel full of energy and well-being.

Balance in the Stimulated Region

Your successful performance results from a perfect balance between challenge and mastery. You set yourself just the right degree of challenge to match your capabilities and ability to handle the situation. Three other ingredients are also important and need to be in balance.

Confidence

Your belief in your ability to achieve the task. The belief is realistic, which helps you to undertake the necessary preparation to achieve the task.

Commitment

Knowing what you want and going out to achieve it. You need to manage the balance between focusing on the future, to give you energy and direction, and paying attention to the present to maximize performance.

Control

You need to focus attention, and act, on what you *can* control, in order to maximize performance. Avoid focusing attention on factors beyond your control and ending up frustrated and unsuccessful.

How to spend more time operating at peak performance

The way to operate at peak performance is to ensure you have optimum confidence, control and commitment. Working on any of these factors will enhance the other two and help you to perform more effectively. Listed below are a number of suggestions for developing optimum confidence, control and commitment.

Developing optimum confidence

1 Learn to handle fear.
Fear is the biggest obstacle to developing confidence. It drives you to panic or causes you to freeze. You cannot operate at peak performance if you have any fears.
2 What are typical fears which may hold you back?

Non-specific fear

Sometimes you may be afraid, but unaware of what you it is that you fear.

Fear of failing

This is the fear which holds people back the most, but the fear itself is more a block to confidence than making the odd mistake.

Fear of the size of the task

When you are stressed any task or situation grows out of all proportion. When you are confident the task assumes normal proportions and becomes achievable.

3 Recognize the warning signs of fear.
Tune in to your own conversations. Everyone talks to themselves.

Your talk is likely to become negative and to lack confidence when you are afraid. This causes you to panic or freeze.

You also respond in a physical way. Look back at the physical warning signs of stress – these are the same when you are fearful.

4 Stop.
Take time to collect yourself and evaluate the situation rather than going headlong into it.

5 Assess the situation.
You need to assess how difficult the situation is and make an assessment of your own capacity for meeting it. This focuses you on action, i.e. what you have to do to manage the situation.

This enables you to become more in control of the situation and switches your attitude from negative to positive.

Developing optimum commitment

1 The first stage in developing commitment is to find out whether you are doing what you like doing. Make a list of how you spend your time and assess how much you enjoy these activities. You will never gain commitment to things you don't like doing. You might need to change the things that you do in your job, or even the job itself, if you lack commitment.

2 Try daydreaming to find out what you would really like to do. Take time out to indulge in a little fantasy. Gradually, realistic ideas can be formulated, and you can then set short-term goals for turning your dreams into reality.

3 Learn to find the right balance between dreams for the future and achieving current goals. You can quickly become over-committed and panicky if you focus too much on future dreams. Alternatively, lack of dreams and too much focus on today means that you are likely to lose direction and become lost in day-to-day activity. The peak performer focuses on goals to maintain direction, and focuses on the present situation to maximize performance. By developing optimum commitment you will obtain pleasure from what you are doing, feel more in control and increase your self-confidence.

Developing optimum control

1 Learn what you can control and what is beyond your control.
You *can* control your immediate situation and how you respond
to it. If other people are involved they are beyond your control –
you can only influence their behaviour.
2 Positive thinking is not enough to acquire control. You need to
give yourself directives that you can act upon immediately. The
action needs to be such that it will direct you towards your goal
and improve your performance.
3 Focusing on what you can do now increases your control over
the situation and builds confidence.
4 Learn to anticipate situations rather than worry about what
might happen. This enables you to prepare for the event, rather
than do nothing and be in a negative frame of mind when the
event occurs.
5 Maximize the situation when the unexpected happens. Learn to
do the things you can do rather than focusing on what has
happened which is beyond your control.
6 Learn to handle the anger which develops from focusing on
situations outside your control. Anger dissipates when you
concentrate on doing things within your control.
The three factors reinforce one another. Developing commitment
helps to increase self-confidence. Developing control also
increases self-confidence and vice versa.

You probably now understand the relationship between
pressure, performance and stress. A certain level of pressure
which generates a certain amount of stress is necessary to achieve
peak performance. Those of you who operate with excessive
pressure are likely to be too out of control to achieve peak
performance. You are most likely to become burnt out by stress.

Those of you who keep the level of pressure down in your lives
are also unlikely to achieve peak performance. Without a certain
amount of pressure you lack the stimulation and challenge
necessary for achievement. Feeling bored can create stress. Faced
with failure or boredom you either adjust and operate erratically,
or turn your anger inwards. In the latter case you will suffer from
the stress of frustration.

The aim of this step has been to help you use the energy derived from stress in a more positive way. To gain maximum benefit you need to spend time reflecting on a situation where you are under-performing and to develop a plan of action for putting the ideas into practice. The questions listed below may help with your planning. When you have completed the exercise proceed to Steps Nine and Ten to help reduce excessive stress levels.

Exercise: optimizing stress levels

Focus on a situation where you are under-performing and answer the following questions:

1 In general is your competence level for the situation:
   too high
   optimum
   too low?

2 In general is the level of challenge you face:
   too high
   optimum
   too low?

3 Refer back to Figure 8 on page 105 which shows the relationship between performance, demands and capability. How do you feel you are reacting to the situation?

- flight reaction
- fight reaction
- stimulated reaction.

Once you have identified your reaction to the situation, follow the steps you need to take to move either from fight or flight to a stimulated reaction. Enhancing the stimulated reaction has already been adequately covered earlier in this step.

Moving from flight to stimulated reaction

- Identify ways in which you could take some risks in the situation.
- How could you stretch yourself more?

- Follow the steps for building self-confidence outlined on pages 110–1.
- If apathy has come about from doing the same job for a long time, what could you do to change the situation?

Moving from fight to stimulated reaction

- Train yourself to stand back. Take time to plan and prepapre.
- Channel your energies to achieve goals – what might be suitable goals in the situation?
- Follow the steps for achieving optimum control outlined on page 112.

Step Nine:
Recognizing ineffective coping strategies

Many of the managers I interviewed realized that they often chose the wrong coping mechanism for managing their stress levels. This exacerbated the problem. At times of high pressure their main concern was survival and their reaction to the situation was inappropriate.

Step Nine will help you recognize the strategies generally found to be less effective for managing stress. Recognition is half the battle. Once you know the less effective strategies you can learn to adopt the more successful strategies and techniques described in Step Ten.

Exercise: Recognizing ineffective coping strategies

Think back over the last two or three years and focus on the stressful times in that period when you failed to manage stress. Then read the descriptions of the methods commonly adopted by the managers I interviewed. Do any of them resemble the methods you have used?

Faced with excessive stress you can adopt one of four broad strategies:

1 Ignore it.
2 Flee from it.
3 Fight it.
4 Manage it.

In the short term all of these alternatives are possible and will protect you from the harmful effects of stress. Long term, the first three strategies are ways of avoiding the core problems. Step Ten will help you to develop management strategies which are more likely to have long-term benefits. First, you need to be able to recognize the less effective methods. Six of those most often mentioned by managers will be described.

Less effective strategies

1 Escape from the stressful situation – withdrawal

One way of coping with stress is to retreat. As one manager said, 'I literally feel as if I want to go away and hide from the situation.' Withdrawal was mentioned when symptoms of stress were discussed. Absenteeism from work is a common sign that a person is under stress. This does provide you with the opportunity to be away from the workplace, a useful strategy if you are suffering from overload. When you return, the problems that caused the stress in the first place are still likely to exist, which makes it a less successful strategy.

A positive approach, if you feel you need to be alone from time to time, is to plan a day a month working at home. Alternatively, if you are unable to work at home, find an activity which enables you to withdraw from your normal day-to-day contact with people. You need to have time each month when you can step back from the demands made upon you by others.

2 Deny that stress exists – denial

Denial is a difficult strategy to recognize in yourself and much easier to observe in the behaviour of others. Some managers spoke of colleagues who refused to acknowledge that they were suffering from stress. One described the attitude of his boss, who said, 'To admit to suffering from stress is a weakness, an inability to cope with the situation.' Those who deny the existence of stress continue to drive themselves, rather than take steps to manage the situation.

You may adopt this approach if you are an ambitious manager. When your performance starts to fall off as a result of excessive stress you are likely to work harder to compensate and repress the signs of stress. This approach is likely to exacerbate the problem and has been shown by research workers to be correlated with stress-related illnesses.

If you realize that this is a strategy you adopt the sooner you stop using it and adopt a more suitable one the more effective you will become.

3 See your problems as other people's problems – projection

The projection techniques means you attribute your problems to others. Using this strategy you may say to yourself, 'Other people around me – colleagues or spouse – are suffering from stress but I am not.' If you have ever been on the receiving end of this strategy you will know that it is a powerful technique – you may actually start to believe that you are suffering from stress. This approach creates misery for others and doesn't help your situation to improve much either. Obviously, you need to accept that you are suffering from stress and start to manage it more effectively.

4 Become obsessional about achieving routine work

If you find part of your job stressful you may channel your energies into routine or unimportant tasks to help block out or avoid the cause of your stress.

If you adopt this approach you may indulge in ritual behaviour or do routine work. You may start to do work that could easily be done by a secretary or a subordinate. To avoid falling into this trap you should assess what you have achieved each week. Ask yourself if you have been doing tasks more appropriately completed by others.

5 Work harder

So far the strategies described have been attempts to avoid or escape from stress. A great temptation, particularly if you are an Ambitious Type, is to work harder when you are suffering from stress. This is an attempt to fight stress and is likely to result in exhaustion. Once you suffer from stress you work less effectively and, in your desire to achieve, are often tempted to work longer hours to complete your job. This is not the way to perform effectively. You just become swept up in a spiral of taking longer and longer to achieve less and less. To break the spiral you must be firm and give yourself time to assess your situation and do those things that help you to achieve your goals.

6 Change to a different work task

A popular strategy adopted by managers is to change tasks when work becomes stressful. Again, the problem that created stress doesn't go away. You utilize the energy created by stress to work on a different task. This can be a reasonably good way to rechannel the energy but at some stage you need to address the original problem.

You are now familiar with common ineffective coping strategies. To complete Step Nine answer the questions below. If necessary, refer back to Step Seven where you identified your own coping mechanisms.

1 Make a list of the ineffective coping mechanisms you have used in the past.

2 Is there any way that you could adapt the ineffective methods to make them more effective?

When you have completed Step Nine turn to the next step to help develop more effective strategies for managing stress.

Stage Ten:
Strategies to remedy imbalance

There are ten strategies which can be used to manage stress effectively. In Step Seven you identified the issues to be resolved. This step helps you select appropriate coping strategies for yourself.

To complete Step Ten, study the list of ten strategies below. The list tells you where each strategy could be helpful. Your task is to select suitable strategies to meet your needs. Then turn to the appropriate page and read the detailed description of how to apply the coping strategy. If the first choice doesn't seem to meet your needs, study the list again for a more suitable alternative.

You will find the strategies easy to understand but difficult to apply! Nevertheless, persevere. If you are to learn the vital skills of stress management it is imperative to put the techniques into practice.

Strategies to remedy imbalance

Read the list of ten strategies. When you have done this, rank the strategies in order of usefulness to you.

Strategy One: Review your relationship with your job (page 123)

Useful if:

- you are not utilizing your full potential
- your stress is related to your job/career.

Strategy Two: Develop your self-management skills (page 125)

Useful if:

- you are currently experiencing overload
- you feel out of control
- you seem to lack direction
- you are unsure what you want out of life
- you are guilty of wasting time.

Strategy Three: Improve your emotional management (page 129)

Useful if:

- you find emotional problems stressful
- you tend to react emotionally to problems
- you are unable to manage your emotions successfully at present
- you direct negative feelings inwards.

Strategy Four: Manage relationships more effectively (page 133)

Useful if:
- you currently have difficulty relating to people
- you have diifficulty being assertive
- you lack the support and friendship you need from others
- you have difficulty handling conflict.

Strategy Five: Improve your problem-solving approach (page 137)

Useful if:

- you still feel unsure of the exact problem
- you feel you would have handled the situation better if you had given it more thought earlier
- all other strategies have failed!

Strategy Six: Develop your physical stamina (page 140)

Useful if:

- you have diagnosed this as the problem
- you face excessive demands in your life
- you lifestyle is not well balanced.

Strategy Seven: Assess your outlook on life and develop a more positive stance if necessary (page 141)

Useful if:

- you tend to adopt a negative approach to life
- the cause of stress is largely self-imposed.

Strategy Eight: Develop techniques for reducing the negative effects of stress (page 145)

Useful if:

- you suffer from tension
- you seldom relax at present.

Strategy Nine: Develop an effective approach to managing change (page 148)

Useful if:

- you diagnosed a high level of change in your life
- you have recently undergone a major change.

Strategy Ten: Seek outside help if necessary (page 150)

Useful if:

- you are experiencing a high level of distress.
- you are unable to resolve the problem yourself.

Ranking the strategies

	Page	Rank
Strategy One	____	____
Strategy Two	____	____
Strategy Three	____	____
Strategy Four	____	____
Strategy Five	____	____
Strategy Six	____	____
Strategy Seven	____	____
Strategy Eight	____	____
Strategy Nine	____	____
Strategy Ten	____	____

Now read the detailed strategy you have ranked number one.

Strategy One: Review your relationship with your job

Observe a group of managers doing similar jobs. Some seem totally at ease in the situation and appear to perform well within their competence. Others seem to be perpetually struggling to meet the demands of the situation. One strategy for managing stress is to be in harmony with your job.

Stress can arise when you perceive that you lack the capacity for meeting the requirements of your job. When this happens your strategy for managing stress may be to diagnose where your capabilities fail to meet the demands.

In essence you have a career-management dilemma. You need to adopt a systematic approach to identifying your current career problem and, if necessary, try to find a work role which fits your capabilities.

1 The first step is to complete an audit of your current competencies. A competency may be:

knowledge
ability
trait
self-image
motive
social role

All these characteristics underlie observable behaviour.
List your competencies in the space below.

2 List the competencies needed to perform the job.

3 Ask yourself:

- Do you lack the capabilities and resources for doing the job?
- Is the situation too demanding?
- Are you expecting too much of yourself?
- Are other people making unrealistic demands on you?
- Is your assessment of yourself too severe?

4 If you *are* being too hard on yourself, or expecting too much of yourself, turn to Strategy Seven. This strategy will help to reduce self-imposed stress.
5 If you lack capabilities, turn to Strategies Two, Three, Four and Five and see if they are helpful. Alternatively, think of action you could take to develop specific capabilities.

If you decide to look for a career which fits your capabilities, one of the best approaches described is that in *Managing Your Own*

Career by Dave Francis. See Further Reading, page 159, for more details.

Strategy Two: Develop your self-management skills

If you study several people you will realize that individuals spend time very differently. Some operate in a frenzy of activity, are always time-driven and never seem to have any spare time; others seem to do very little. The successful self-manager has learnt to have time for work and leisure; time for activity and for reflection. He has achieved balance in his life and views time as money.

The skill of self-management

You need to work through a number of key stages to manage yourself successfully:

1 Planning.

- Set clear goals. Decide what you want to achieve in life – this helps you to operate effectively, rather than reacting to situations as they arise.
- Set short-term and long-term objectives. Decide what you need to do to achieve your goals – this helps to convert plans into actions. To keep you motivated make sure that your objectives are achievable.
- Develop action plans. This gives you a schedule of work which relates to your goals. You don't just do tasks that you enjoy, or that happen to crop up.

2 Use time effectively. Time can be managed effectively or wasted. The latter situation is most likely to happen unless you manage yourself.

First, you need to find out how you are spending your time already. Completing the exercise at the end of this section will help you.

You can then establish whether you waste time. You may do this for a number of reasons:

a Interruptions from others.
b Disorganization.
c Failure to delegate.

d Reacting to crises.
e Unclear objectives.
f Too much to do, with unrealistic deadlines.
g Tasks left unfinished.
h Lack of self-discipline.
i Lack of system of priorities.
j Procrastination.

A study of this list of common time-wasters will help you to use time more effectively. There are a number of rules you need to follow:

- Spend time quietly the day before or at the start of each day making plans of how you will spend the day. Make a list of everything that needs doing
- Establish a clear system of priorities.
- Leave aside some time each day for unplanned activities.
- Make time each day for completing your own activities.
- When you are working make sure you concentrate fully on the task.
- Delegate as much as you possibly can.
- Never put off till tomorrow what can be done today.
- Schedule periods of relaxation and thinking-time.
- Don't let planning dominate, leaving no time for work.
- Be realistic about achievement – don't fall into the trap of becoming a perfectionist.

3 Learn to pace yourself. People who have learnt the skill of self-management are able to pace themselves effectively. Avoid working excessively hard all the time. This is certainly likely to be a problem if you are an Ambitious Type. Schedule time, if necessary, which enables you to relax and recharge your batteries. This makes you more likely to maximize performance.
4 Achieve a balance in your life. A common source of stress is failure to achieve a balanced life. If you are to manage yourself effectively *and* cope with stress, you need to ensure that you are taking care of needs at work *and* in your private life. Completing the exercise at the end of this section may help to highlight any inadequacies. Those of you who have children, as well as demanding jobs, need to create time for yourselves. You may find

that your whole life is spent taking care of responsibilities at work or at home, leaving no time for yourself.

5 Review progress. Review the progress you have made after three months. Are you still experiencing difficulties in any particular area? Are there further changes which you need to make to manage yourself effectively?

Finally, one study showed that people who adopted a strategy of compartmentalizing 'work' and 'home' were less likely to suffer from stress-related illnesses. There is often a temptation to work late or take work home. Try to discipline yourself to leave work at the office. If you cannot, at least be strict with yourself and don't allow work to encroach too much into leisure time.

Exercise to develop effective self-management

Complete the following time-log over the period of a week and fill in work and home activities. Self-management can be applied at home as well as work.

Once you have completed the time-log for a week, review it.
Perhaps also discuss it with colleagues and your spouse.
Then answer the following questions:

1 Am I performing any unnecessary tasks?

2 Do I give the right amount of time to tasks that help me achieve my objectives?

3 What are my long-term goals over the next five years?

4 What are my goals for the next six months?

5 How much time did I waste in the week?

6 Could I delegate any tasks?

Day	am			pm			eve		
	Activity	Priority: High or low	Time wasted	Activity	Priority: High or low	Time wasted	Activity	Priority High or low	Time wasted
Mon.									
Tue.									
Wed.									
Thu.									
Fri.									
Sat.									
Sun.									

7 Do I have an adequate balance between work and leisure?

8 What specific changes am I going to make?

This exercise will help you to improve self-management. If you seriously mismanage yourself you may need to attend a time-management course to help develop this skill.

Strategy Three: Improve your emotional management

If you are able to manage your emotions effectively you are able to control your feelings and keep them appropriately balanced. To enhance wellbeing and invulnerability to stress you also need to be able to display emotions and avoid a build-up of negative feelings.

In Step Six, emotional reactions were identified as a way of spotting the signs of stress. You may know people who always remain calm, and others who appear calm but are in fact hiding the turmoil going on inside. You probably also know people who give vent to their feelings by swearing, slamming doors or having angry outbursts. This strategy will help you to exert control when it is appropriate.

The skills of emotional management

1 Understand the situation. What gives rise to your emotional reaction? Understanding the cause of your feelings is the first step towards control. The second step is to understand why you feel the way you do. A useful approach is to view your feelings as being created by your thoughts and the way you interpret events – your internal dialogue. You may not be able to control events but you can control your internal dialogue. This gets your feelings much more under your control. Negative feelings mean that you are having negative thoughts – your feelings follow your thoughts. You may think your feelings genuinely reflect reality, but they reflect your *interpretation* of reality. The most helpful way of identifying your internal dialogue is to write it out on paper.

2 Identify your likely emotional response to a stressful situation.
In Step Six I explained that you are likely to experience one
or two feelings more regularly than others. Different emotional
responses require different forms of management – you need to
select the right method.

● Depression, apathy and withdrawal. From the outside this is a
fairly passive emotion. The emotion is directed inwards. Energy
needs to be redirected outwards. This requires you to become
active to reduce the emotional reaction. Sometimes emotions such
as these stem from physiology – the noradrenaline level in the
body can become lowered. A useful management strategy is to
engage in physical activity, such as swimming or running, which
will lift depression.

● Anxiety. This is the flight response to stress. The core of this
emotion is worrying, whether it be about catastrophes which might
happen, your fear of achieving goals, or fear of taking examinations. The way to cope with this emotion is to face up to the
inevitable – you live in an uncertain world which is full of things
you can worry about. You have a choice: to spend life worrying,
frequently about things beyond your control; or to adopt a more
philosophical attitude to life, live more in the present and focus
on activity, rather than living in the future or looking back on the
past.

● Anger. This is the fight response to stress. It is the emotion
that you might experience when you feel frustrated, for example
when someone has done you an injustice or has been spreading
malicious gossip. Given free rein it can damage relationships.
Allowed to build up inside you it causes physical damage. How
can you cope with this emotion? Understand that the emotion
stems from your perception of the situation, change that perception and the emotion will change. Channel the energy from the
anger into an activity, for instance play a game of squash, to
release the tension.

3 Develop the capacity to control all emotions. Learn to channel
the energy they generate into some form of activity. This is known
as displacement activity and can be an effective way to cope with

stress. The important thing is to avoid undue stress caused by remaining too long under emotional pressure.

4 Delay reacting emotionally. When you are about to have a negative outburst, count to ten. This helps you to think rationally rather than behaving emotionally and avoids having damaging effects on other people.

5 Release emotional tension in the right place at the right time. In the privacy of your own home is usual. This technique is used in Japan, when employees release tension on a punch bag. You can develop your own version of this! It is a far more effective way to give vent to your feelings than off-loading on an innocent person.

Exercise – improve emotional management

Think of a recent emotionally stressful situation and answer the following questions:
1 Describe the stressful situation in as much detail as you can.

2 What emotions did you experience?

3 What were the thoughts which gave rise to these emotions?

4 How did you react in the situation and what were the consequences of your reaction?

5 Did you attempt to manage the stress you experienced? If so, what did you do and was it successful?

6 Describe how you will manage an emotionally stressful situation next time it occurs.

7 What messages could you give yourself when the situation occurs to help avoid mismanagement? (Possible messages could be 'think before you act', 'don't over-react' or 'don't panic!')

If you are over-emotional two other strategies may help you restore the balance:

- Strategy Five may help you tackle the problem more rationally.
- Strategy Eight may help reduce the build-up of emotional pressure.

Strategy Four: Manage your relationships more effectively

Being successful at managing your relationships means you are able to relate to people well, ask for what you want, meet your own social needs and handle conflict effectively. Relationships at work, with family and friends, were identified as a common source of stress. Successful management of relationships will help you cope with stress in three ways:

1 It will develop your support mechanisms and make you more resistant to stress.
2 It will cope with a major stressor.
3 It will help prevent the build-up of negative feelings.

To manage relationships successfully you need to be able to:

- make contact with people
- listen
- assert yourself
- handle conflict

● take responsibility for yourself/protect yourself.

1 Make contact with people. At work and at home you often need to interact with people you have never met before. Many people are basically shy and find this initial contact difficult to handle. You will interact more easily with practice and by following a few basic rules.

● Encourage the person to talk by asking questions.
● Show genuine interest in the person.
● Give positive encouragement and recognition to the person by smiling and nodding.
● Focus your attention on the other person instead of your own discomfort.
● Admit to ignorance – people enjoy talking if you encourage them.

Activity

Each week practise making contact with as many people as you can. If you find conversation difficult, practise the art with people you know well.

Watch people who interact freely and learn from them.

2 Listen. If you listen carefully to people you hear what they are saying and feeling. This enables you to empathise with them, to put yourself in their shoes and experience their feelings. The rules for making contact also apply to listening. In addition, you need to:

● Really concentrate on what people are saying.
● Watch the non-verbal cues. Feelings usually come across non-verbally.
● Check understanding from time to time by summarizing what you have heard.

Activity

Practise your listening skills each week by observing the rules outlined.

After a few weeks the depth of communication and the overall quality of your relationships should improve.

3 Assert yourself. When you assert yourself you are able to:

- Ask for what you want.
- Say no without feeling guilty.
- Confront issues you might otherwise evade.
- Stand up for your rights.

Learning the skill of assertiveness will greatly reduce the stress level of the nonassertive person, who may experience resentment when he cannot say no.

To become more assertive you must:

- Learn to respect and value yourself.
- Practise assertive answers so that they come freely.
- Be prepared to say what is on your mind instead of bottling up your thoughts and feelings.
- Learn to stand up for yourself and stand your ground in difficult situations.

Activity

Make a list of all the situations in the last month when you failed to be assertive. Alongside each situation write down how you could have handled the situation assertively.

In the next month practise handling potentially problematic situations in a more assertive way.

4 Handle conflict. If you are able to handle conflict, differences of opinion will be resolved with ease and without bad feeling on either side.

To resolve conflict skilfully you need to:

- Identify the problem clearly and discuss it so that there is common understanding. Conflict can arise around facts, attitudes, personal values, invasion of personal space or roles.
- Learn the art of compromise – to be more satisfied with less – by:

a Practising trusting the other person and adopting a cooperative stance.
b Identifying the problem in a way that is resolvable – sometimes in a conflict situation the issue can grow out of proportion.
c Learning to meet the other person halfway.
d Learning to relax when conflict arises. When you are in conflict you become emotionally aroused. When you are very emotional you cannot think rationally and you become preoccupied with your own position and unable to see the problem from the other person's perspective.
e Learning to see the problem from the other person's viewpoint.

Activity

Identify a relationship which matters to you and in which conflict has arisen. Reflect back on an example of conflict. Write down how you handled the situation. Using the guidelines above, how could you have handled the situation differently?

5 Take responsibility for yourself/protect yourself. To manage relationships effectively you need to adopt an independent stance to life and to be able to take care of yourself.

To achieve this you need to:

- Value your own independence and that of the other person.
- Be happy within yourself and not depend on others to make you happy.
- Learn to become resourceful.

Activity

Set yourself three goals that will help you develop a more independent stance. Give yourself one month to achieve the goals, then review your progress.

Strategy Four has given you some guidelines to help you manage your relationships more effectively. This is a complex issue. You may benefit from looking at two further strategies – Strategy Three and Strategy Seven. There is also Further Reading on page 158.

Strategy Five: Adopt a problem-solving approach

You may have reached this stage in the book and still lack a clear perspective on what is causing you stress. If this is the case you may benefit from adopting one of the problem-solving approaches described below. You could either tackle the problem-solving alone or adopt a proven creative approach with a group of people you can trust. In each case you progress through a number of stages.

Approach One: Problem-solving alone

This approach is useful if you do not wish to share the problem with others. You may benefit from putting your thoughts and feelings down on paper as you work through the steps listed below. This helps you to clarify your thinking and provides you with a useful source of reference for the future.

Stages in problem-solving

1 Identify the problem clearly. You need to be as specific as possible at this stage. For example, you could say your job is causing you stress, and the problem then becomes your job. Having analysed the situation more carefully you might then say that the problem consists of 'handling conflict with one of your subordinates'. This is more focused and is more likely to result in a solution to the problem. Redefining the problem further, it becomes 'engaging in conflict with your subordinate results in a reduction in his sales figures'.

2 Collect data of relevance to the problem. List all the available facts and, if possible, talk to people connected with the problem. For example, under what circumstances does conflict arise; what happens when conflicts occurs; do you experience similar conflict with others; does your subordinate experience conflict with others; what steps have you taken in the past to resolve the conflict?

3 Analyse the data you collect. At this stage you could talk to people who are uninvolved. They may be able to give a more objective analysis of the situation.

4 Generate possible solutions to the problem. Write down as many ideas as possible. Solutions could include:

- leaving the situation
- altering the situation
- removing the stressor
- altering your perception of the situation.

Try to develop the solutions in a fairly detailed way.

5 Evaluate the alternatives and select a solution to the problem. Some of the solutions will be impractical when you consider the implications.

6 Develop an action plan. Write down the steps you propose to take to manage the problem. You must also lay down criteria for success.

7 Implement the action plan.

8 Review the outcome.

Approach Two: Problem-solving in a group using brainstorming

You need at least three people to use this approach.

What is brainstorming?

Brainstorming is a process designed to bring out into the open as many ideas as possible on a given topic without censoring contributions. Working in a group, people stimulate one another, and more ideas are generated than when you work alone. The prevention of censorship stops people from evaluating ideas. What at first seem like wild ideas can often be developed into practical, creative solutions.

How to brainstorm

1 Have a warm-up session first. A popular exercise is to generate as many uses as possible for a paper clip. People call out their ideas and someone writes them down on a flip chart. People call out at random and no one is allowed to evaluate contributions.
2 Once the ideas have been generated, go back and evaluate them.

When you have had this warm-up session, work through Approach One, in the group, using brainstorming to help complete stages one and four.

Approach Three: Handling the 'spaghetti problem'!

This approach is particularly helpful when you are experiencing emotional stress generated by several issues. Under these circumstances you become unable to think rationally, your perspective may become distorted and the issues become woven together (rather like spaghetti).

   Tension builds up until it reaches the stage where it cannot be contained. This can often happen at weekends when you relax and get in touch with your feelings. In this situation you may find Approach Three helpful.

1 Externalize the issues, preferably by talking with a friend or counsellor, or write them down. Bring all your thoughts and feelings out into the open at random.

2 When you have finished step one, identify all the issues and draw up a list.
3 Deal with each issue separately using the problem-solving approach described above in Approach One.

This approach has three benefits:
1 It releases tension.
2 It helps you to think rationally.
3 It provides you with an action plan that helps you manage your emotions.

Strategy Six: Develop your physical stamina

You will have established whether you need to improve your physical fitness in Step Two (pages 21–7). By tackling this problem you should raise your energy levels and develop your capacity to resist the demands placed upon you. You may also find that being fitter alters your perception of situations. Again, this is likely to make your life less stressful.

There are several steps you need to take to improve your physical stamina and overall fitness level.
1 Follow a sensible diet. This was covered in Step Two. To recap you need to:

- eat regular meals
- avoid too many snacks
- eat as much fresh food as possible
- restrict your intake of sugar, carbohydrate, red meat and added salt.

2 Monitor your drinking and smoking habits. Again, this was mentioned in Step Two. If you are trying to improve your physical stamina this should be included in your action plan.

3 Maintain the appropriate weight for your height. You are more likely to develop illnesses such as high blood pressure and coronary diseases if you are overweight. If you have a weight problem you will have to overcome it if you want to improve your physical fitness. You will need to take more exercise and eat the right food in the right quantities.

4 Follow a programme of exercise. Most managers, particularly at times of excessive stress, find it difficult to take adequate exercise. Exercise should be taken regularly and should be within your capabilities. Avoid violent exercise when you are unfit. Following an exercise programme with others might help you stick to it more easily.

To be physically fit you need to take some form of exercise two or three times a week. Do something you enjoy if you can. What are the available options?

- a sport such as jogging or swimming
- weight training
- a programme of exercise
- brisk walking, possibly to work.

5 Allow adequate time for relaxation and rest. People vary in the amount of sleep they need. Most medical experts agree that approximately seven hours sleep is desirable. Quality of sleep is also important and is likely to be improved if you are able to relax before going to bed. You probably need to assess the quality and quantity of your sleep over a period of time to ensure it is adequate.

If you suffer from tension you may benefit from following Strategy Eight, which helps to reduce the effects of negative stress.

6 Review the balance you achieve between home and work. A balanced lifestyle is a necessary component of any fitness programme. Taking more exercise and giving yourself time to relax should help ensure a balanced life.

7 Take regular holidays. There is no substitute for a properly planned holiday. A complete change allows you to relax fully and build up your stamina.

Further reading on diet and exercise can be found on page 158.

Strategy Seven: Assess your outlook on life and adopt a more positive stance if necessary

Two men looked out of the prison bars,
One saw mud and the other saw stars.

Viewing life in a positive way – adopting a positive stance to life –

is a valuable stress-management strategy. As the quotation above demonstrates, most situations can be interpreted in at least two different ways. Depending on your perception, the situation may be seen as more or less stressful.

Strategy Seven is split into two stages:

Stage One will help you to assess your current stance. If you have selected this strategy to study in more depth, you may be concerned that your outlook on life is rather negative. If this is the case, Stage Two is designed to help you develop a more positive approach.

Stage Two will describe five main steps to be taken in order for you to become more positive. Once you have completed Stage Two you will be more able to manage excessive stress by influencing your perception of the situation.

Stage One: Assessing the stance you take towards life

Exercise: Analysing situations

Think back over the last week and make a list of all the situations you viewed negatively. Alongside your list of situations write down your negative thoughts, feelings and attitudes.

How stressful were the situations you have listed?

How many situations were you able to list?

If you had great difficulty thinking of any, your approach to life is probably fairly positive already. If you have listed at least two incidents you are likely to benefit from the second stage of the strategy, particularly if you assessed the incidents as stressful.

Exercise: Discuss your approach to life with others

In addition, or as an alternative approach, you may like to talk with friends or colleagues to obtain an outside assessment. This will give you useful information on the way you present yourself to others. Their views will help you form a more detailed assessment of yourself.

Stage Two: Steps to develop a more positive approach

Some people seem able to rise above any situation and remain positive. These people are usually good at managing stress. Others have to learn to become more positive by dropping the habit of adopting negative feelings and meanings. Listed below are some exercises designed to help you become more positive. You may be able to add some of your own.

There are five key steps:

- Let go of the past if necessary.
- Adopt positive meanings and feelings.
- Practise giving yourself positive messages.
- Develop a positive approach to others.
- Enjoy the present.

1 Let go of the past if necessary. Certain events in your past may be colouring the way you experience life today. Everyone experiences failures and disappointments, but if you are unable to let go of the past it will stop you from enjoying today and making the most of new opportunities. You may be thinking about previous jobs, relationships or dreams that never materialized.

Make a list of all the things that you still relive from the past. Make a decision to let them go and channel your energies into living for today.

2 Adopt positive feelings and meanings. Go back to the list you made in Step One of this strategy. Alongside each negative thought, feeling and attitude write a positive thought. This starts you thinking in a more positive way.

List the important stressors in your life at the moment. Write down a positive meaning for each stressor.

When you find yourself being very negative, write down all the negative points. When you have done this write a positive alternative alongside each one. Next time you find yourself being negative, think of the alternative positive meaning. Learn to count your blessings. There are always others around who are less fortunate than yourself.

3 Practise giving yourself positive messages. You are likely to have an internal dialogue with yourself. You can either build yourself up by giving yourself positive messages, or exert considerable internal pressure on yourself through negative messages.

What messages do you give yourself?

If your messages have a negative effect try some of the techniques listed below to reduce the pressure.

Put a list of positive messages on an index card. Next time you feel under excessive stress read the index card. If you are giving yourself the right messages you should feel better.

Are you laying a trap for yourself? For example, if you say to yourself 'I haven't the skills to do this job' you are far more likely to fail than if you say 'I will rise to meet this challenge.' Try to list as many of the traps you lay for yourself as you can. When you have done this give yourself a positive message in its place. In future you will then deal with the traps by adopting a positive response.

4 Develop a positive approach to others. If you adopt a positive approach to others they are far more likely to reciprocate. Much of the advice given in Strategy Four will help you to be positive. Relating to others positively enhances your feeling of wellbeing.

Select a day and be as positive as you can, giving as many positive messages as possible to others. Again, this becomes a habit and you will feel much better.

5 Enjoy the present. You may spend so much time regretting the past or worrying about the future that you miss out on the present. You have most control over the present, so maximize the opportunities that are around you while from time to time keeping an eye on future goals to ensure you have direction. By concentrating on the present you can maintain a better balance between activity and feelings.

Log a day and identify how much time you spend in the past, present and future. Whenever you are negative bring yourself back to the present and monitor what happens. You are likely to achieve more and feel much more positive. Develop your own mechanisms for staying in the present.

Once you have worked through these techniques you should develop a much more positive approach to life and increase your enjoyment of situations.

Strategy Eight: Develop techniques for reducing the negative effects of stress

When you suffer from excessive negative stress you become very tense and blood pressure rises. The stress reaction was fully discussed in Step Three (pages 34–46). One successful strategy is to adopt relaxation techniques which will help reduce your level of tension and enable you to cope more effectively with the pressures of life.

There are several different techniques available. To master some of them you would need to attend classes. These are described briefly to familiarize you with the methods. First, progressive relaxation and meditation are described in a little more detail as these are both techniques you could teach yourself.

Progressive relaxation

This is a straightforward approach to relaxation. It is designed to reduce tension by helping you to control your breathing and relax your muscles.

Procedure

1 Sit in a comfortable position.
2 Close your eyes
3 Starting with the muscles in your face, clench the muscles then relax them.
4 Relax all your muscles, from head to toes, in turn. Keep the muscles relaxed.
5 Become aware of your breathing. Count as you breath in and out: breath in, 'one, two, three', breath out, 'one, two, three'. Breath easily and naturally.
6 Continue for ten to twenty minutes. At the end of that time open your eyes and get up after a few minutes.

Conditions

1 Practise the technique once or twice a day, but not for at least two hours after a meal. The digestive process seems to interfere with the relaxation response.
2 A quiet environment should be chosen with as few distractions as possible.
3 Try to adopt a passive attitude. Don't worry about how well you are relaxing. To avoid distractions and maintain a passive attitude keep repeating a word or visualize an object. This will stop your mind from wandering, which prevents the relaxation response.

Meditation

Meditation takes relaxation a stage further by diverting the mind from everyday thought processes. You are required to focus your attention on a mental picture, a word, a real object or a sound.

Meditation requires practice, and you probably need to master relaxation first. Once you are able to meditate, you are likely to become calmer, have a more alert mind and become less stressed.

Procedure

1 Adopt an appropriate position – standing, sitting or kneeling – keeping your spine straight.
2 Keep your body still until the end of the exercise. This helps to achieve the physiological benefits already mentioned, as well as the psychological benefits of increased self-respect and confidence.
3 The simplest form of meditation involves concentrating on an object. This can be imaginary or an actual object.
4 Discard any thoughts which enter your mind.
5 At first you will only be able to concentrate for a few seconds. Keep practising until you can concentrate for about ten minutes. When you can concentrate for this length of time you will relax, your anxiety level will be reduced and the elimination of psychosomatic illnesses will be helped.

Other techniques

Yoga

This is another technique for relaxing body and mind and reducing stress. Your whole body is gradually exercised through correct breathing and the adoption of particular body postures. If you want to practise yoga you would be well advised to go to classes.

The Alexander Technique

This technique involves adopting correct body posture, and standing, sitting and moving correctly to reduce muscular and physical tension. It is an excellent method for reducing stress, but rather lengthy training is required to achieve maximum benefit.

Relaxation tapes

Several tapes are available to help build self-esteem and assist relaxation and stress reduction. Alternatively, you may find listening to music more relaxing.

Jacuzzis, whirlpools and baths

A very effective way to ease tension is to soak in a hot bath at the end of the day. Alternatively, a jacuzzi or whirlpool actually massages the body and is another good form of stress reduction.

There are a range of techniques available for reducing tension and stress. Relaxation exercises can even be practised for five minutes sitting at your desk at work. You need commitment to practise the exercises at first, but once they become part of your daily routine you will be amazed at the results you can achieve.

Strategy Nine: Develop an effective approach to managing change

Throughout life you are constantly faced with change. You may have diagnosed a high level of change in your life in Step Five. Successfully managing change may help to reduce your stress level.

Change can occur in several ways, but ultimately you have to develop new ways of thinking, feeling and behaving in order to deal with it. Change may be self-imposed or forced upon you. It may happen suddenly, such as the death of a relative, or be gradual, for example your job may alter over a long period of time.

To manage change effectively you can either:

● understand the stages through which you progress to achieve change

or

● use the technique of forcefield analysis described in Step Seven.

Stages of change

The stages of change and their relationship with performance are shown in Figure 9.

Stage 1: Freezing

At the time of change there is an initial period of shock, particularly if the change is for the worst. Work performance is low at this stage.

Stage 2: Denial of change

People often deny to themselves that any change has taken place. This is partly to protect themselves from fear of the unknown and

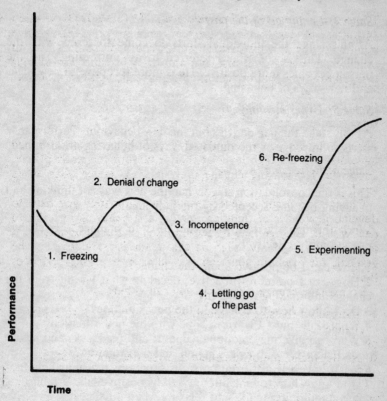

Figure 9 **Stages of Managing Change**

to help them cope with the situation. For a short time performance improves but then it falls off and the person reaches Stage 3.

Stage 3: Incompetence

This is sometimes referred to as 'The Peter Principle'. The person is under-performing; unless he lets go of old ways of behaving and adapts to the change, performance is unlikely to improve.

Stage 4: Letting go of the past

At this stage the individual starts to come to terms with the change. This is sometimes referred to as 'unfreezing' and the person becomes more positive. He is more receptive to new ideas and new ways of behaving.

Stage 5: Experimenting

At this stage the person tries out the new behaviour. Performance starts to improve as the outdated ways of behaving are dropped.

Stage 6: Refreezing

This is the consolidation stage when the new ways of thinking and behaving become accepted by the individual.

Work through the following checklists to manage this change process more effectively:

1 How can I be positive about the change?
2 How can I be more proactive, deciding what I want from the change and making it happen?
3 Do I know how to behave in the new situation?
4 What skills must I learn to cope with the new situation?
5 Who can give me emotional support and feedback, and advise and challenge me to assess myself and the situation?
6 What have I learnt from previous situations that may help?
7 Do I know how to look after myself by positive talk, establishing some stability in my life and relaxing when possible?
8 Do I know how to establish priorities and set objectives?
9 Can I see positive opportunities?
10 Have I learnt from the situation?

Strategy Ten: Seeking outside help if necessary

In certain situations you may need to obtain help from an outsider. This is particularly advisable if you are suffering from a high level of stress and you are unable to find a solution.

What are the advantages of outside help?

- The person who gives advice is not emotionally involved and can take an objective view.

- If you seek help from an expert the problem may be solved more quickly.
- You may feel more comfortable discussing your problems with a relative stranger.

What are the alternatives available?

1 Your doctor can advise you. If your problems are psychological, counselling may help. There are counsellors attached to hospitals who can provide this service.

2 If your problem is job-related, a career counsellor would be the best person to approach.

3 For other specific problems, such as divorce, alcoholism, bereavement and drug dependence, I would recommend the Consumers' Association publication *Living With Stress*. This includes many useful addresses and telephone numbers from which you can obtain further help.

Part 4
Managing the Balance

Step Eleven:
Your stress-management strategy

The purpose of this step is to identify what you need to do to implement your strategy and establish a plan of action. By writing down the steps you will increase the likelihood of success. You would also benefit from sharing your action plan with a friend or colleague.

To help develop your plan of action answer the following questions:

1 What is the specific issue/problem you are going to tackle? (Try to be as specific as possible and don't be too ambitious.)

2 Set yourself a clear, specific objective. (For example, to improve your fitness level by taking more exercise.)

3 Lay out a plan of what has to be done to achieve your objective.

4 To implement your plan what specific changes in behaviour will you need to make?

I will do more

I will improve

I will start to

I will do less

I will stop

5 What do you do already which helps you handle the isssue/problem?

6 What support do you need from others, and whose support do you need?

7 In the space below write some personal messages to help you when the going gets rough.

8 How will you know when you have successfully implemented your strategy?

You are now ready to implement your plan. Take it a step at a time and don't be put off if it takes longer to achieve the results than you had anticipated. Good luck with managing the balance.

Further reading

Managerial effectiveness

John Adair *Effective Decision Making* Pan (1985)

Thomas J. Peters and Robert Waterman
In Search of Excellence Harper and Row (1985)

K. Blanchard and S. Johnson *The One Minute Manager* Fontana (1981)

K. Blanchard, P. Zigarmi and D. Zigarmi *Leadership and the One Minute Manager* Collins (1985)

M. Woodcock and D. Francis *The Unblocked Manager* Gower (1982)

Relationships

Wayne W. Dwyer *Your Erroneous Zones* Sphere (1976)

Thomas Harris *I'm OK, You're OK* Pan (1973)

A. and T. Harris *Staying OK* Pan (1985)

M. James and D. Jongeward *Born to Win* Signet (1978)

D. Stubbs *Assertiveness at Work* Pan (1985)

M. Smith *When I Say No I Feel Guilty* Bantam (1975)

Managing change

A. Toffler *Future Shock* Pan (1971)

Stress

A. Melhuish *Executive Health* Business Books (1978)

Living with Stress Consumers' Association (1982)

R. Kriegal and M. Kriegal *The C Zone: Peak Performance Under Pressure* Anchor Press (1984)

Diet and exercise

Vogue Complete Diet and Exercise Book Octopus Books (1985)

Relaxation

M. Gelb *Body Learning: An Introduction to the Alexander Technique*
Aurum Press (1981)

L. Chaitow *Relaxation and Meditation* Thorsons (1983)

J. Madders *Stress and Relaxation* Martin Dunitz (1979)

Careers

D. Francis *Managing Your Career* Fontana (1985)

Index

Peter F. Drucker
Management £3.95

Peter Drucker's aim in this major book is 'to prepare today's and tomorrow's managers for performance'. He presents his philosophy of management, refined as a craft with specific skills: decision making, communication, control and measurement, analysis – skills essential for effective and responsible management in the late twentieth century.

'Crisp, often arresting . . . A host of stories and case histories from Sears Roebuck, Marks and Spencer, IBM, Siemens, Mitsubishi and other modern giants lend colour and credibility to the points he makes' ECONOMIST

The Practice of Management £3.95

'Peter Drucker has three outstanding gifts as a writer on business – acute perception, brilliant skill as a reporter and unlimited self-confidence . . . his penetrating accounts of the Ford Company . . . Sears Roebuck . . . IBM . . . are worth a library of formal business histories' NEW STATESMAN

'Those who now manage ought to read it: those who try to teach management ought to buy it' TIMES EDUCATIONAL SUPPLEMENT

Managing for Results £2.95

'A guide to do-it-yourself management . . . contains first-class suggestions that have the great virtue that they are likely to be widely and easily applicable to almost every business' TIMES REVIEW OF INDUSTRY

'Excellent . . . well-supported examples of what has happened in practice to companies that have thought in this analytical way' FINANCIAL TIMES

Managing in Turbulent Times £2.95

This is Peter Drucker's latest and probably most searching analysis of the problems and opportunities facing us as managers and individuals. This timely and important book considers how to manage the fundamentals of business– inflation, liquidity, productivity and profit – going on to demonstrate how tomorrow's manager must concentrate his skills on managing innovation and change – production sharing, new markets, redundancy planning, the developing countries, transforming businesses to take account of changes in the world economy.

Derek French and Heather Saward
Dictionary of Management £4.95

A handy reference work providing definitions for nearly 4000 terms, abbreviations and techniques current in general and functional management and in such areas as government, law and economics that affect the manager's work. An indispensable source of information for managers, students and interested laymen who wish to extend their understanding of the modern business world.

John Hunt
Managing People at Work £3.50

Here, at last, is a lucid analysis of recent developments in sociology and psychology and their implications for managers. John Hunt presents, in a readable form, relevant ideas from the major areas of organizational behaviour: motivation, perception, communication, groups, roles, power, organizations, structures, managers, leaders, participation and change. His objective is to let managers decide for themselves whether behavioural tools can be useful and valuable to them.

Michael Edwardes
Back from the Brink £3.50

'Essential reading for anyone who struggles to understand the realities of our commercial condition' ROY HATTERSLEY

'He sees things clearly and simply. He has an exciting story to tell and he tells it brilliantly' THE DIRECTOR

'In five years he succeeded in transforming BL. Its products are more reliable and imaginative, its economic performance is better, its factory efficiency second to none in Europe' THE TIMES LITERARY SUPPLEMENT

'Learn the lessons well' DEREK ROBINSON